Anne Jordan-Hoad is the pen name of the divorced wife of a former Baptist minister. She is a qualified nurse, midwife, health visitor and further education lecturer.

Throughout her professional life, but especially as a divorced mother, she has wrestled to understand the relevance of faith to life's dilemmas. Her interest in writing began as a student nurse when she cycled to London on her days off (15 miles each way) to help in the Christian Literature Crusade office.

She has written for church magazines and professional journals. This is her first published book.

She recently took ill-health retirement from the NHS and lives in London.

# COME
# TO ME

Biblical mothers with
contemporary problems

A<small>NNE</small> J<small>ORDAN</small>-H<small>OAD</small>

TRIANGLE

First published in Great Britain 1998
Triangle Books
Holy Trinity Church
Marylebone Road
London NW1 4DU

*British Library Cataloguing-in-Publication Data*

A catalogue record of this book is available
from the British Library

ISBN 0–281–05160–7

Typeset by Pioneer Associates, Perthshire
Printed in Great Britain by
Caledonian International, Glasgow

# CONTENTS

———————————

# FOREWORD

The Bible is full of the most marvellous stories. They display a range of experience and feeling that would have the writer of best-sellers and the most lurid tabloid journalist alike howling with envy. The Bible includes just about every *genre*, from stories of passionate lovers overcoming tremendous obstacles to political thrillers of intrigue and treachery, from quiet pastoral narratives to epic journeys, from comic streetlife to dark and sombre accounts of famine, slaughter and rape. But there are two problems that can peculiarly limit the power of these stories for us.

The first might be described as the problem of *too little* knowledge. Because so many of them take place in times and places so distant from our own, and tell of a culture, faith and way of life in which many details are terribly hard to grasp, new readers can sometimes be discouraged from discovering these old stories, can think of them as obsolete, irrelevant to *our* lives.

The second might be described as a problem of *too much* knowledge. So familiar are these stories to some of us, from childhood even, that they have become over-familiar, stale. We think we know everything they have to tell us, they have lost their power to be new.

Therefore, we need people like Anne Jordan-Hoad who, in retelling these marvellous stories from a fresh angle, helps us to get over the barriers of time and space that separate us from them, *and* gives them the newness, the unfamiliarity that attracts our attention, catching us up into the story as if for the first time. It is like sitting down with someone eager to tell us about what happened because 'I was there'. There is no greater spur to the imagination.

Anne Jordan-Hoad is telling many stories – but she's also telling one story, the story of mothers! Mothers often get overlooked, and yet there is probably no relationship so significant for every human being, man or woman. There are many stories of mothers in the Bible, and indeed, God our Creator is described as motherly. How interesting to hear many of these stories from the perspective of the mother. And so skilfully drawn are their landscapes, that we can feel the burning heat on our backs, the pain of hunger or thirst; with our senses we can feel the dough for the bread in our fingers, catch the scent of desert flowers or of perfumed oils, taste the sweet water. We are never far from the physical here, continually reminded that for these women over several thousand years, some things remained constant. The daily tasks of care for a household, the endless repetition of provisioning, cooking, washing; these are still a large part of *my* life and the lives of women all over the world.

Here too are the spiritual and emotional struggles of motherhood; the desire to do and see the best for one's children; the pain of giving them up in the many ways that women *do* have to let their children go; the difficulties and the remarkable joys of single motherhood; the agony of the mother who watches her child suffer, and the equal or greater agony of the one who watches her child become the cause of suffering. 'Was it my fault? Did I do all I could?' After all, they are not so different, these women.

One cannot help but be moved by that particular anguish of motherhood, the woman who is unable to bear a child. These women too are mothers, praying to God for a child, or, if not a child, some other creative form of mothering to be given to them. Here, we have deep insight into the childless woman *and* the surrogate mother, in a culture in which bearing children was the only legitimate task and expectation for women.

And with these mothers, as with mothers today, the struggle also to be *themselves*, to be mothers, and yet to be women with their own stories, identities, loves, faults and longings for God. We may not agree with all the interpretations, or like all the women. That does not matter so much. What matters is that, in reading their stories, the distances recede, they become women whose stories go beyond the limits of culture and geography and time, into a place where we can stand beside them, in fellow feeling, in compassion. This is what makes the difference.

*'And of some have compassion, making a difference'*
(Jude 21, Authorized Version).

Kathy Galloway

# ACKNOWLEDGEMENTS

I should like to thank Naomi Starkey at SPCK for giving me the opportunity to write this book and for her indispensable advice and guidance on the way. I also want to thank my vicar, the Revd Nicholas Holtam, my friends Julia Honey and Dorothy Walker, my fellow writers in the Square Circle and at the University of Kent (Tonbridge Centre) and our mentor Charlie Bell for all their encouragement; Richard Harper, Director of the British School of Archaeology in Jerusalem, for access to the library; Walter and Leah Reimer for chauffering me around Upper Galilee; the Little Sisters of Sion in Jerusalem, for their kind hospitality; Rabbi Sybil Sheridan for reading the manuscript and making invaluable suggestions on biblical history texts; and Susan Dunsmore for reading and advising on the manuscript on behalf of SPCK.

Scripture passages quoted are taken from the Good News Bible published by The Bible Societies/HarperCollins Publishers Ltd UK © American Bible Society, 1966, 1971, 1976, 1992, 1994.

*For my sons*
*Keith and Mark Jordan*
*and their families*

# INTRODUCTION

Come to me, all of you who are tired from carrying heavy loads, and I will give you rest. Take my yoke and put it on you, and learn from me, because I am gentle and humble in spirit; and you will find rest. For the yoke I will give you is easy, and the load I will put on you is light.

(Matthew 11.28–30)

In this book I take an imaginative look at ten of the mothers we find in the Bible. Mothers with problems like ours: infertility, illness, hunger, homelessness, ambition, disappointment, surrogacy and adultery. I have tried to show how God meets them, how they respond to him, in their everyday experiences. They are ordinary women who live extraordinary lives because the core of their being is directed to God.

The book is a work of fiction but I have made every effort to be true to the text and to such archaeological, cultural and geographical evidence as is available. I have at times modified some details of ancient Eastern culture to make the stories easier for the modern Western reader to understand. My hope is that this book might encourage readers to go to the original text with new enthusiasm. I hope they might discover, or rediscover, the Bible as a living book about real people which can be relevant to their modern daily life.

I am also writing in celebration of motherhood. The greater part of my professional life has been spent working

1

with mothers, both as a midwife and as a health visitor. In my personal life I found myself left alone to cope with two children of pre-school age. I believe, passionately, that motherhood is a vastly under-rated vocation in modern society. I hope this book will help to redress the balance. I hope we shall look with new eyes at this privileged and sacred task. It can be the most thankless, exhausting and heart-breaking job in the world, yet it can also bring the deepest joy and fulfilment. It is a sacrificial calling and I believe we ignore that at our peril.

It has become unfashionable to talk about sacrificial living. As a Christian mother I find it helpful to think of a candle in my response to the living God. In these days of electricity we keep candles in the back of the cupboard in case there is a power cut. Or we use candles for romantic, decorative or festive occasions. Electricity makes us forget how dependent we are on light. We take it for granted. A candle, whether plain or beautiful, cannot fulfil its true purpose of giving light until we put a match to the wick. To give light it must burn. To fulfil its purpose it must be consumed, it must 'die'. In truly loving relationships we all have to 'die' a little. That is, we put the needs or desires of the loved one before, or at least equal to, our own.

If possible, I would like a burning candle to be at the heart of these meditations. Find a quiet space in your day either in the morning or the evening, at work or at home, to read a chapter. Switch off the television and disconnect the telephone and any other sources of distraction, light a candle and sit absolutely still, in silence, observing it for five minutes at the end of reading each chapter. Try not to pray. Try not to think. Studying the dancing flame will help to silence your mind. In the stillness God can speak to you.

The book is intended for private devotional use, which is why the prayers are written using the personal pronoun, but there is no reason why it should not be used by a group in public or in the home and the prayers adapted accordingly.

2

# 1

# FAITH AT SEA

*Noah's wife stands by him
against the odds*

---

> Do not be afraid – I will save you. I have called you by name –
> you are mine. When you pass through deep waters, I will be
> with you; your troubles will not overwhelm you.
>
> (Isaiah 43.1, 2)

They sit hand in hand, in comfortable silence, on the
gently rocking deck; the taste of salt on their lips, the smell
of the ocean in their nostrils; the only sound the soporific
slap, slap, slap of water on wood. On the horizon the sun,
an enormous orange globe, gradually slips from sight.
There is no land to east, or west, or north, or south.

She squeezes his hand and he turns to study her face
in the failing light. In his eyes she's as beautiful now as she
was the first time he saw her in her father's yard. She was
milking the goats, he remembers; her skin was like ivory,
her hair like flax ready to harvest. He'd been the envy of
the village when she agreed to become his wife. Now
her ageing wrinkled face is etched with grime from the
long voyage, but he doesn't see that. To him every line and
furrow portrays her inner character, represents the joy of
the years they have spent together.

'No regrets?'

'No regrets.'

'I'm not such a silly old fool then?' The corner of his mouth turns up with the quizzical look she knows so well. The years haven't dimmed the light in his eyes nor the reassuring smile he gives her.

'I'm sorry. I didn't understand.'

'Neither did I!'

Their eyes meet and they both laugh, remembering. She watches him as he carefully lights the lamps along the walkway before joining her again. He picks up the sprig of olive which had been resting on his knee, pensively twirling it round in his fingers. Together they study it, not speaking.

'The dove didn't return today.'

'No,' she pauses, 'What does it mean?'

'It means we have a difficult task ahead of us,' he answers with the suspicion of a sigh.

'You mean we do not have a difficult task at present?' she teases.

He smiles and says nothing then, 'The dove has found land. It means we must disembark and find a suitable place to settle down again. We shall need to quarry stones to build homes, till the land and sow the grain we brought with us. It will not be easy. I've grown accustomed to the relative peace of life at sea. I enjoy the leisurely pace of life on board, travelling with the currents, drifting with the winds.'

'Braving the storms and blistering in the sun!' she laughs. 'I shall be glad to get my feet on solid ground again. But you are right. It's not going to be easy. We have our sons and their wives to help us,' she takes his hand, 'and we have each other.'

'It's not going to be easy, is it?'

'We've got a lot to be thankful for.'

'Yes . . . Yes, we have.'

She shivers in the evening air, drawing her shawl closer.

It's getting dark now but they are reluctant to go below. The last few weeks have been a welcome respite after all the terrifying months. Turbulent months. The days ahead will be difficult. The past is like a bad dream; the future, uncertain; the present moment, too precious to waste in sleep.

Zillah studies her husband's profile. He's changed. It is not easy to say how; his beard is a little longer, a little greyer, but it's not that. In spite of everything he seems more settled. A year ago (was it really only a year ago?), it was very different. He was withdrawn, irascible, troubled by his own thoughts and unwilling to confide in her. Then his behaviour had become . . . a smile begins to creep across her frowning face; she begins to chuckle softly.

'Do you remember their faces when you started?'

'Could I ever forget? You weren't very complimentary yourself as I remember.'

'You can hardly blame me.'

'Well, to be honest, I felt pretty foolish.'

'You did? I'd never have guessed!'

'It wouldn't have done any good to let you know I was worried. I wasn't sure I was doing the right thing. It seemed absurd even to me.'

'I really thought, you know, that everything had just become too much for you: the harassment by our neighbours; your opposition to the forces of evil; dishonesty in the market place, despotism and intrigue, bribery and corruption by our leaders, murder and injustice, sorcery, lotus eating and lewd behaviour, and many things too terrible to mention, had finally overcome you. I feared an evil demon had taken possession of you. I thought . . . I thought . . . I thought . . . I don't know what I thought. I was terribly afraid. I thought I'd lost you.'

'I know. I did try to explain, Zillah. You must admit that.'

'Explain! You said, My dear, I've been talking to the Lord Elohim . . . !'

'And so I had.'

5

'Yes, I know that now! It was hardly reassuring at the time. Especially when you told me what he said!'

They sit in silence for a while. The evening breeze is fresh with an unusual fragrance, evocative of happy childhood days. It is the scent of olive trees. Finally Noah speaks, his voice low and solemn, 'It was good of you to stand by me.'

'I couldn't do much else, could I?'

'Well, you did, and I'm glad of it. You're a good woman, Zillah.'

He holds her hand gently and they lapse into silence again.

'What's he like, Noah? Elohim? You've never told me.'

'No, I haven't told you. It would be too difficult to put into words . . . He was like, well, not so much a form as a presence . . . like wind on water. I don't know how else to describe him.'

'Weren't you terrified?'

'Terrified? I don't know . . . It all happened so quickly somehow. I was too surprised to be afraid.'

'What did he say, exactly?'

'He said he was repelled by his creation . . . that he had made a mistake . . . it had all gone wrong . . . it was flawed,' Noah pauses, deep in thought, before continuing, the words seeming to stick in his throat, 'He said he wished he'd never thought of making mankind.'

'How terrible! . . . Did he sound angry?'

'More sad than angry, I think.'

The lamplight flickers on their faces and they stare into the darkness beyond the deck.

'It's dreadful to imagine. What if we should ever feel like that about our sons . . . Regretting they'd ever been born.'

'Yes.' He pauses for a long time. Then, unexpectedly, he begins to laugh. 'It all took some believing, didn't it?'

'It wasn't so bad when you drew up the plans but when you started felling the trees and preparing the wood I was really worried.' She joins in his laughter.

'Yet you encouraged the boys to help me.'

'We thought we should humour you . . . and it seemed harmless enough. But then, when you prepared the pitch, the smell, and the mess! . . . and you explaining that you had to waterproof the vessel . . . and not a drop of water in sight!' The words tumble out through her laughter.

He replies more seriously, 'I kept thinking, what if I've got it wrong? Supposing it was just a dream? No, I'm not surprised you doubted my sanity. I doubted it myself at times.'

'Then, the animals!' His wife laughs again. She laughs and laughs until tears roll down her cheeks. Noah watches for a while before a slow smile spreads across his face and he joins in her laughter at the absurdity of it all. They sit, rocking with laughter for several minutes until Zillah, drying her eyes, becomes serious again, 'The worst thing was the way the neighbours gossiped. I hated that, especially the sniggering.'

'Well, they have learnt their lesson the hard way.'

'There's no satisfaction in that. Those last days, when the rains came, were terrifying. I still see the flood waters and hear the howling winds and roaring waves, and the screams, in my sleep.'

'They could have repented. The Lord Elohim spared us. He would have forgiven them, too.'

'It's so tragic . . . so horrific . . . I shall remember every detail of those dreadful days as long as I live. The death and destruction, the terror, the annihilation of every living thing; as long as I live. I wish I could forget,' she murmurs. 'In spite of everything, I wish we could have helped them, Noah.'

'There was nothing we could do. They had their chance. We must thank God we are alive, trust in his mercy for the future.'

She sighs, 'The future . . .'

'Look at the heavens, Zillah. The stars are very bright

tonight.' They both look up. There is a full moon rising in the sky now and the sea looks silver in its gentle radiance.

'Look how the moonlight shimmers on the water.'

'It's like a footpath, sparkling and dancing, leading to the sky.'

'It's an omen. The Lord Elohim is with us. We must follow such light as we have.'

'It might lead us to the stars.'

'So it might. Are you afraid?'

'Not with you, Noah.'

He picks up the lamp and hand in hand they make their way to their sleeping quarters.

The land is dry now. After many busy weeks of disembarkation and resettlement, life has settled into a comfortable routine. The survivors of the flood are occupied from dawn to dusk; Noah and his sons spend their days tending the animals and fishing while the women attend to the land and look after the dwellings. Zillah's favourite occupation is to sit at the door, spinning, looking out over the lush green valley below and the mountain slopes above. The once barren floodswept hills are ablaze with colour. Wild iris, poppies and lilies have colonized the land.

Every day, at dawn, Zillah accompanies Noah to offer a sacrifice at the altar he built in thanksgiving for their deliverance. She feels as if the sun is always shining. She has almost put the dark days before the flood out of her mind.

'The Lord Elohim has blessed our sons, Noah,' she declares one morning.

'He has blessed us all.'

'Yes, I know . . . but, I mean . . . he has *blessed* them.'

'Blessed them?' Noah looks at her.

'We shall soon have the sound of children in our home again,' she says, hugging him, her eyes sparkling.

'Well, now,' he remarks, and after a moment, with a broad grin, 'that calls for a special offering today!'

With light hearts they begin to go down the mountain. As they turn to go a fierce east wind blows up. Dark stormclouds gather in the distance and rapidly approach the tiny settlement, obliterating the sun. It grows cold and overcast. Terrified, Zillah clings to Noah's arm.

'Noah, Noah,' she cries, 'look at the heavens! It's going to rain. There's going to be a storm. See how black the sky is!' She begins to cry. 'I cannot bear it. I cannot bear it. Surely it cannot happen again? Not now.'

'Hush, woman.' Noah takes her in his arms. 'Look. Look over there.'

She follows the direction he is pointing to but can see nothing because of her tears.

'Dry your eyes, and look. See, there.'

Zillah dries her eyes and looks again in the direction of Noah's outstretched finger. There is a tiny break in the black clouds and an arch of light stretches right across the valley. It covers the land like a bridge between earth and heaven; transparent, but multicoloured. Zillah had never seen colours in that way before. Red, orange, yellow, all blending into one another so that it is difficult to see where one ends and the other begins; then green, blue, indigo and violet.

'Oh, Noah,' she can hardly speak. 'It's beautiful. What is it? What does it mean?'

'It's God's promise to us. One day when I was in his presence there was a rushing wind. After that I saw fire lighting up the heavens and the voice of thunder stalked across the sky. Then, in the stillness which followed, he spoke to me. He made a solemn promise to humankind, never again to destroy the works of his hand. Whenever stormclouds gather, if we look, we shall see his bow in the sky. A sign of his promise to us.'

'It's lovely. What is it called?'

'It has no name.'

Together they gaze with wonder at the vision. Zillah feels safe in Noah's arms.

9

'The Lord Elohim's promise in the skies. His bow of many colours in the heavens, shining through the rain clouds, to give us hope.'

'A rainbow. It is a rainbow.'

'Thanks be to God, the Lord Elohim, whose promise is sure for all generations.'

### PRAYER

*Lord of creation, give me grace to trust you when storm-clouds cover my life and I am afraid. When the world seems dark and forbidding, help me to hold on to belief in your love and goodness. Help me to acknowledge my anger and fear and to channel these emotions into positive action.*

*Give me grace to praise you when the sun shines. Give me grace to trust you when it rains. Give me grace to remember you in every rainbow. Amen.*

*Suggested reading*

Genesis 6.5–14; 7.1–10; 8.1–12; 9.8–15.

# 2

# THE SURROGATE MOTHER

*An Egyptian slave receives
God's blessing*

———⟨⟨⟨⟨●⟩⟩⟩⟩———

> Even before they finish praying to me, I will answer their
> prayers.
> (Isaiah 65.24)

I wake just before sunrise and dress quickly. It is a cold, grey morning in early spring, but nothing can dampen my spirits. A bubble of joy gurgles inside me as I hurry outside the tent to fetch water from the storage jars. My mistress, Sarai,* is awake and calling impatiently that I should come to her. I have been her slave since I was a child.

The sun is rising and happiness wings my feet as I go to her, swiftly and silently setting about my duties. I help her to put on her robe then she sits before me on a woven stool. Picking up the ivory comb I can barely suppress a smile. Using my fingers to separate the tangled strands, I work it gently through her hair. Long dark hair, dyed black to disguise her age, beautifully oiled, sleek and shining. I am mesmerised, watching the creamy white teeth of the comb part the thick black locks; watching my hands

---

*See p. 21.

deftly braid and bind the unruly mass into a neat plait. My mind is far away.

'What are you smiling at?'The sharp voice jars me back to the present. Let her scold me, I no longer care. I have a secret.

'Smiling, Madam? I did not know I was.'

'You are smiling. What are you smiling at?'

'I did not know I was smiling, Madam.'

'Do not be insolent. You are smiling. I command you to tell me what amuses you so much. Tell me or I will beat you.'

'I am sorry, Madam. Maybe I am just smiling because I am happy. It is going to be a lovely day and I enjoy my work. I am lucky you chose me to be your personal maid. Many of the other servants envy me, you know, Madam. I love dressing your hair; it is so beautiful.'

My answer silences her, as I knew it would. Her hair is magnificent, and she is very proud of it. Reluctantly I have to admit, because she has not borne children, she is still a shapely woman. In her youth her beauty attracted the great Pharaoh. He fell in love with her and took her to his harem before he discovered she was married to Abram.* What a furore it created! The gods were angry and sent terrible illnesses to punish him, so Pharaoh made retribution to Abram, presenting him with sheep, and slaves and rich jewels, begging him to take his wife and leave the country. I was given to Sarai as part of her compensation. I was just 10 years old. My mother was a maid to the ladies of the harem and she was training me to follow in her footsteps. I would have liked that. My life in Egypt was very pleasant, very civilized. Now I roam from place to place with these wandering people. I dwell in the wilderness in foul-smelling tents, far from the cultured life I knew as a child.

My mistress jerks her head impatiently, turning to glare

---

*See p. 21.

at me, 'Be careful. You are pulling too tightly. Keep your mind on what you are doing.'

Her voice cuts into my thoughts like a whiplash, then, looking keenly at me she continues, 'Are you sickening for something? You have been wandering around in a dream for days.'

I have been her maid for a long time and we know each other very well. It is difficult for me to hide anything from her, but I am determined not to tell her my secret. Not yet. Not until I have to.

'I am sorry, Madam. There is nothing wrong with me. I was thinking about the feast we had for the King of Salem. It was very good. The master was so pleased and you looked splendid, Madam.'

Again my answer silences her. It really was a magnificent feast. I continue to plait and fasten her hair and return to my musing.

My master is a wealthy man with many camels and other livestock and a very great household. We are forever searching for fresh pasture for the animals. It is a nomadic life. My mistress boasts that one day we shall settle in a land promised to my master by his god. A god greater than any god of Egypt, she tells me. This god, called El Shaddai,* spoke with my master face to face. It is hard to believe. Not even the great Pharaoh has spoken face to face with a god! El Shaddai promised to give my master a new land, a fertile land, lush and green with room enough for all his cattle. I cannot imagine any land more fertile than the land of Egypt, and certainly we cannot settle there.

My mistress also brags that the same god, El Shaddai, promised my master many descendants. Well, that may

---

*I have tried to reflect the many names by which God has been known to his people at different times. This is the name likely to have been used by Sarai and Abram.

be, but it will not be by her. I admit she is still a handsome woman but she is far too old to have a child. I smile to myself again. For all her wealth and privilege, I am the one who will fulfil the promises of her god. It was her idea that I should sleep with her husband and bear his son for her. She does not know yet that her wish is to come true. I shall bear her son for her but, for the present, it is my secret. While she does not know I am expecting a baby, it is mine. I want to experience the joy of bearing new life for as long as possible before she takes it from me. As soon as the child is born, she will claim it as hers by right of ownership. It is not fair. I am the one who has been chosen. Her god has made me fertile, not her. I am the one who has been given life. I shall keep it secret and treasure it while I can. It is worth putting up with her insults; until my pregnancy begins to show.

Even though I must give up the child, things will be different. My master will be pleased. He will reward me with fine clothes to wear; my mistress will have to treat me more kindly; and my son will have his inheritance.

My son? Supposing the child is a girl? I cannot allow myself to think of that. But, if it is, why then, I shall have proved my fertility and my master will try again to have a son by me. I will sacrifice to the gods. I will visit the sorceress and exchange jewels given to me by Abram for secret herbs. I will do all I can to ensure I bear a male child.

Sarai jerks her head impatiently and reaches for the leather strap she uses to beat me. Scowling at me she says, 'Wake up. You are daydreaming again. Keep your mind on your work. And do not think, because I have allowed you to sleep with my husband, that it changes your position here. Now, be about your duties. Quickly.'

She strikes me sharply. I duck. The blow misses me. Dressed in all her finery, my mistress goes to supervise the household and I am left to my daydreams.

Carefully I open the cedar box and start to replace the

14

containers; ivory applicators and intricate kohl pots, carved spoons, and other trinkets. My favourite is the make-up spoon in the shape of a girl swimming. As a child in Egypt I used to swim often in the Nile but here, in this desert, there is no water. I run my fingers lightly over the lovely form, wondering about the craftsman who shaped it. I remember, long ago, my father used to carve ornaments for me. Where is he now, I wonder? Where is my mother? They will never know I carry their grandchild. Hot tears well up in my eyes and spill down over my cheeks. I taste the salt. But it will not do. I must not give way to my unhappiness because the wise old women of my land say a sad mother gives birth before her time and brings trouble on her child. Picking up the heavy bronze mirror I gaze at my reflection, brushing away my tears I talk to myself, as I often do, 'Do not be discouraged, Hagar. Take heart. Things will be better. You will be a mother and have new status. Even though Sarai will claim the child, you will be the rightful mother. Do not fret any more.'

I smile at the face peering out at me. I think I see an unusual glow, a radiance about my face which I haven't noticed before. My skin is clear and my eyes bright. I have to admit to myself that I am quite good-looking in my own way. If I were to be dressed in the same silks and linens as my mistress I might be considered beautiful. On a sudden impulse I sit on Sarai's stool and begin to outline my eyes with the jet black kohl. Fine eyes I have – huge with long black lashes. I am still admiring myself when an angry voice screams at me, 'What do you think you are doing?'

Too late, I leap to my feet and try to shield my face against the blows which I know will follow. The leather strap stings as it catches me. I feel the warm trickle down my cheek and taste the blood which runs into my mouth. The lashes come one after another, thick and fast, as I stumble and fall. No-one heeds my cries; no-one dares.

15

It is night. I wake from a troubled sleep, exhausted still from too much crying. My body smarts and aches from the beating my mistress gave me. I creep out of my blanket and hastily gather together my few belongings, cautiously wrapping them in the blanket. I carefully stow away some bread, cooked eggs and coriander seeds which I saved from the evening meal. With great unease I place the silver necklace, amulets and ear rings I have stolen from my mistress, jewels she seldom wears and will not readily miss, in my shawl and wrap them up carefully. Finally, I tuck my treasured figurine of the goddess Maat into my linen pouch. She has been with me and watched over me since I left the land of Egypt. I make my way stealthily out of the sleeping quarters, taking care not to wake anyone. Heart pounding, I cross behind the other tents and eventually reach the boundary of the encampment. No-one hears. No-one sees.

I do not know where I am going. I do not know what I am going to do. I only know I must get away. I cannot think beyond that. I must escape.

I understand, at last, that my mistress knows my secret. It dawns on me, finally, that, although it was Sarai's intention to have me bear her husband's child, now that her plan is working she is jealous. If I remain she will beat me and the child might die. The baby is all I can think about. I must protect it. This child who is not my child. I must escape now, while I can. Where will I go? I do not know. It does not matter. I only know I must go. The gods will go with me.

The night is long and I am worn out with walking. I am cold and tired and hungry and I need rest. I need sleep. When I reach those rocks ahead I may find a cave to shelter in. I thank the gods for a moonlit night.

If there are wild animals about, what will I do? I do not know. I am too tired to worry about it. The gods will surely protect me. I wear my sacred eye on my forehead and my good luck charms around my neck, wrists, and ankles; every talisman I possess. They will surely protect me from any evil spirits or wild beasts hiding in this place. Clutching my figurine, I wrap myself in my blanket and curl up in the entrance of the cave.

I sleep fitfully, hovering in the wilderness of half-waking dreams where I see myself wandering alone on a narrow barren footpath. There is a great chasm on my right, so deep I cannot see the bottom, and on my left craggy cliffs rise up high above me so that I am walking in dark shadows. Ahead of me a dust storm gathers. I am trapped. I am cold and paralysed by panic, fearing to go forward and unable to turn back.

I wake up with a start. The nightmare is so real that I believe it is true. I cannot remember where I am. The hard surface of the figurine I am still clutching in my hand brings me to myself. Wet with perspiration, I shiver. I am stiff with cold. My wounds throb with pain. 'What will become of me?'

But soon the morning sun appears on the distant hills. I freshen my face and hands with my cloak which is damp with dew. I sip water from my leather bottle. There is one egg left in my bag, so carefully breaking and removing the shell I swallow it eagerly. I eat a portion of the bread, too hungry to notice how stale and dry it has become. Anxious that my master's men may be already in pursuit I collect my things together and set off again, heading south. The sun is rising in the sky.

I walk all day, frequently stubbing my feet on the uneven ground. As I stumble along the rock-strewn path, I begin to understand what I have done, and I am afraid. This barren land, home to lions, jackals and other beasts is hostile to travellers. It is a haven for lepers, robbers and bandits, not a safe environment for a woman with child. But, I cannot go back, and I do not regret my flight. So I press on, footstep after weary footstep making my way south, seeking my homeland. But, where is my home? I do not know. I am driven by the same instinct that takes the migrating stork, like white stormclouds, south; always south.

I see no-one all day. My feet burn; my wounds throb with pain. It will soon be night and I must find water and a safe place to shelter. In spite of my resolve, my heart falters.

'Mother of the moon, Father of the Nile, look with pity on your handmaid. Show me the way back to my people,' I say to myself as I walk. Then another thought comes to me and I call out, 'Lord of my master Abram, have mercy on me. Show me the way I should go. Lord, god of my master Abram, make my path straight and show me the way I should go. Have mercy on me. Have mercy on my master's unborn child.'

A voice startles me. I did not see anyone approaching. 'Hagar, slave of Sarai, where have you come from and where are you going?' I hear the voice, but I see no-one. Is it in my head? It sounds too real. Am I delirious?

'Hagar,' the voice speaks again. It is real. The shock of being discovered dries my tears and I hastily wipe my eyes, trying to see who it is who addresses me by name in this wilderness. Has one of my master's servants found me?

There is a stranger standing in my path but his back is to the setting sun so that I cannot see his face.

'How do you know my name?'

'I know you.'

'How can you know me?'

'Never mind how. What are you doing here?'

'I am running away from my mistress because she beats me cruelly. I do not mind for myself, I am used to it. But,' I sob, 'but I am expecting a baby. I fear it may be harmed by her frequent flogging.'

I fancy the stranger looks kindly at me, but I cannot see his face clearly. I can only see his shape silhouetted against the orange glow of the sky.

'You must return,' he says. 'Go back and be obedient to your mistress. Be humble and patient and try not to provoke her. Put up with her insults and abuse for the sake of your child. You will need courage. The path you must tread will not be easy. You will suffer. But El Shaddai will bless you and you will have a son. He will be wild and unruly. A social misfit and at odds with his relatives. But, even so, through him you will become the mother of a great nation. You will call him Ishmael because God has heard your prayer.'

His words have the ring of truth and I kneel before this stranger, believing he must be a prophet.

'Do not worship me but listen to what I say. You must be brave, but you must return. Put your confidence in El Shaddai, and believe.'

He is still speaking when the sun sets, and he is gone as suddenly and as soundlessly as he appeared. I call out to him not to leave me here. There is no reply. I search for him but he's nowhere to be found. It is night now and I am quite alone but I no longer feel afraid. To my surprise I find the embers of a fire glowing in the shelter of a rock. The remains of a meal are lying beside the fire. Gratefully I eat, stirring up the embers and feeding them with small twigs until I have a reasonable fire. I eat. I warm myself. I begin to wonder. Who was the stranger who appeared so mysteriously, called me by name, and vanished so suddenly? Here is food he has prepared for me. I stop eating and regard the chicken leg I hold in my hand. It looks perfectly ordinary. Could he really be a messenger of the Most High, the god of my master Abram? I tremble at the thought. No, he was just on a journey, like myself, showing me the common courtesy of a fellow traveller.

'Then how did he know your name?'

Startled, I look up, to see who speaks, but it is the voice of my own thoughts. He knows my name. He sees me here in this desert place. I am still holding the chicken leg and I look around, expecting the man to appear. Every rock, every blade of grass, every leaf whispering on every tree, all seem to speak to me; to see me.

For the first time I understand that God is a god who sees and understands all about me. Now I know, the god of my master Abram, El Shaddai, is here, he sees me, he knows my name. He watches over me. I have no need to fear him.

For the second night I wrap myself in my shawl and lie on my blanket on the hard ground. But tonight I have the fire to warm me and a good meal inside me. I am too elated to sleep. I ponder my meeting with the stranger, turning it over and over in my mind.

I wake with a start to hear the birds singing. Despite the hard ground I feel unaccountably refreshed and cheerful. A heavy dew covers the earth. The embers of the fire are still glowing, giving off a gentle heat. There's no sign of the stranger but I find a small bag containing barley loaves, figs and dried fish. How very odd. In the darkness of the previous night I hadn't noticed it. I eat with relish all the time turning over in my mind the meeting with the stranger.

I must do as he has commanded. I must return. The thought no longer fills me with dread. El Shaddai will be with me. He knows my name.

The journey back seems shorter than my long trek into the wilderness. I am apprehensive; but at the same time I feel inexplicably tranquil, as if someone is holding me close. I feel safe, even though I am afraid. Nothing my mistress might do to me can harm me. I am, after all, carrying her son for her.

Her son? My son? Whose son? The stranger said the child would be at odds with all his relatives. I wonder what he meant?

Thirteen happy years pass. Abraham* is a kind man. Delighted to have a son, he is good to me, and does not allow Sarah* my mistress to ill-treat me. He provides separate quarters for me to live in, with my son. His only request is that I treat my mistress with respect and serve her loyally. She takes little interest in Ishmael but, though she is cool towards me, she treats me more courteously because of him. She has to. As the mother of Abraham's only son my position has quite changed.

These are the happiest years of my life. I have no reason to believe that anything will change. My master prospers. My son grows big and strong. The household is secure in spite of the tribal wars all around us. Wars which sometimes involve Abraham, taking him away from home for many months at a time.

I no longer think about the prophecy of the stranger I met in the wilderness before Ishmael was born. I do not contemplate the unfulfilled nature of the prophecy. I might not have called it to mind at all had it not been for the three visitors who have come to us.

Three noble travellers, richly dressed and riding upon camels, arrive in the fertile valley where we camp with our flocks. The sun is high in the sky when they appear, riding unexpectedly out of the heat haze which hangs over the desert. I am sitting outside my tent, in the shade of palm trees, weaving. Sarah is in her enclosed area with her women and my master is sitting in the shadow of his tent with Ishmael my son, sharpening flint knives. We know at once, from their swarthy looks and strange apparel, that they have journeyed from a far land. Their appearance is so sudden it startles us.

It is a duty, but also a delight to entertain guests. It gives my master an opportunity to receive news from distant lands, and with what joy he greets them, running to welcome them, shouting orders to left and right that a lavish feast is to be prepared. He goes himself to slaughter a choice calf from the flock.

---

*See Genesis 17. God promises to have a special relationship with the children of Abram and Sarai forever. As a sign of this covenant, God changes their names to Abraham and Sarah and commands that all the men be circumcised.

I help with the preparations and watch the celebrations with interest. Interest, and some apprehension. Something about the way the visitors appear, without warning, reminds me of my encounter with the stranger in the wilderness. Are these unexpected guests also messengers of El Shaddai? I have a sense of intangible foreboding. A dim memory of the prophecy concerning my son, that he would be an outcast from his people. I had forgotten it. Now I have a premonition that these strangers will disturb my peace.

It is true, the strangers are prophets. I am shocked to hear them foretell that my mistress will have a son. Sarah laughs in disbelief, even turning to me, expecting me to share her mirth. But I cannot. Although it seems too fantastic for words, because she is very old, I have a feeling of impending disaster.

Just nine months later she gives birth to a son.

It is the end of my carefree days. Before Isaac, her son, was born she tolerated me, because she had to. Ishmael was Abraham's only son. Now Ishmael has a brother. Sarah's son. She has no need of us any longer.

Now my master says we must leave. Even though my son Ishmael has been circumcised as a sign that he will follow the one true God, like his father Abraham, we are to be banished. All because Sarah, my mistress, is jealous. There is no need. I could never take her place. I wouldn't want to. But she fears for the inheritance. It is so unfair! It is so unfair! My tears fall thick and fast wetting the contents of the bag I am packing.

'Where are we going, Mother?'

'Your Father is sending us away, Ishmael.'

'I know he is. But why? And, where to? I do not understand.'

'Do not ask so many questions. Pack your bags as I told you.'

He turns away, sullenly. His face dark with anger. I do not blame him. I am unable to explain to him the

22

jealousies and intrigues of the adult world. It is too difficult. I barely understand it myself. I know my master, Abraham, does not want to banish us. I see it in his eyes. I see also that he has no choice.

'Do not cry, Mother. I shall take care of you. Never mind them. I hate them!'

Fear, like a knife, stabs my heart. The shock of his words dries my tears. I turn to my son, 'No, Ishmael. You must not hate. It will destroy you. There are things you do not understand. You are too young to understand.'

'I understand that we're being sent away and you are crying!'

'Yes. But that's the way it has to be. When you are older you will understand.'

'I am not a child, Mother. I know what is going on. When I am old enough I shall have my revenge.'

'Ishmael, my son, I am sad and unhappy. I do not deny it. I am afraid of what may lay ahead of us. But, Ishmael, I believe El Shaddai is with us.'

'That does not make sense, Mother. What do you mean?'

'Do you remember the story I told you about the time I ran away into the wilderness, before you were born?'

'When you met the messenger of God?'

'Yes. We will go into the wilderness, but we will not be alone.'

'Do you think the stranger will come again?'

'Yes. Come, I will take you to the place. I believe he will meet us there.'

Once more I pick up my bundle of belongings and start out on the road south. But this time I am not a fugitive, and I am not alone. My son is with me. His father, Abraham, has given us provisions for our journey. The way ahead is difficult and uncertain. I set out into the wilderness, with my son by my side, and trust in the God of Abraham.

23

*Father in heaven, to my limited vision life often seems unfair. I can too easily be resentful and jealous. I am sorry.*

*I thank you that the clouds which often veil my sight, and the doubts which mask my judgement, are sometimes swept aside so that, very briefly, I catch a vision of the glory that is – a deep sense of your presence, your power, your purpose – and my place in the whole.*

*Give me grace to hold on to such moments for the reality they are, so I can be free to see others with a pure heart. With clear vision to gladly rejoice in their success and serenely support them in their distress.*

*For Christ's sake, who always teaches us to look in the heart and not at the outward appearance of things. Amen.*

*Suggested reading*

Genesis 16.1–15; 21.9–21

# 3

# THE MOTHER OF NATIONS

*A doubting woman has a child
in old age*

———

When a woman is about to give birth, she is sad because her hour of suffering has come; but when the baby is born, she forgets her suffering, because she is happy that a baby has been born into the world.

(John 16.21)

The rugged trunks of the palm trees creak in protest against the wind rustling through their branches. My old body creaks and groans too as I wake from a restless sleep. Slowly I rise, shake out the bedding, and hang it to air over a rocky outcrop outside the tent. I shade my eyes to look at the complaining trees, marvelling at the delicate, feathery designs their great leaves make against the blue expanse of sky. So familiar but so varied, like the changing seasons, the changing patterns of life. The autumn rains have passed and the land looks barren, but here, where my husband has pitched camp, we have sufficient water. There is adequate pasture for our cattle, sheep and goats. Although the land is desolate, we are not, because we know how to live with it. We understand it. It is our home.

Many long years we have lived here, moving from place to place, sometimes at peace, often at war, but always prosperous. My husband, who is also my half-brother, is a devout man. A wise man. He seeks peace but is ever prepared for war.

When we were young we lived with our father, Terah, and his several wives in the city of Ur. A wonderful city. Our father was a wealthy merchant and we lived in luxury in stone-built houses with sumptuous furnishings. Twice a day we burnt the incense of thanksgiving to our household gods. Their shrine held pride of place in our home. On special feast days we went to worship at the Ziggurat, the mighty temple tower which the King had built to honour the moon god. At the time we believed the moon god ruled over all the gods. It was a magnificent building which sparkled white and gold in the sunshine and so high I thought it reached up to heaven. I remember it at night too, shining silver, mysterious, in the moonlight.

I was a child when my father Terah arranged my marriage to Abram, the second son of his first wife. What a celebration we had. Those were happy times. Then, one day, our brother Haran died. Father was overwhelmed with grief. Calling us together, he said, 'This is an evil land. I cannot stay here. We will leave and find a better place. We will travel north and settle in a city where the trade routes from east and west, north and south converge.'

But our brother Nahor refused to travel with us, preferring to remain in the land of our birth; so Terah took Abram, our nephew Lot, and all our households, and we set out as soon as the spring rains were over, not knowing what was ahead.

The long trek took us and our laden donkeys over shimmering desert sands, through valleys darkened by the mountain ranges towering above and on, across lush fertile plains which stretched far into the distance. Always the sun beat down upon us from a cloudless, unforgiving sky. I longed for the cool comfort we had left behind. On and on we journeyed, often travelling at night because the days were too hot; always following the northern star.

Looking at the giant palm trees now, as I set about collecting the water skins, I think that perhaps it was fortunate I did not know this was only the first of many such journeys. I make my way to the well, remembering the tedious journey which finally brought us to Haran, where we settled. It was a city similar to Ur, but smaller. We soon felt at home and life was agreeable. We prospered. Here, as in Ur, we and our neighbours worshipped many gods, but when Terah died, Abram became restless again. The voice of an unknown god, mightier than the moon god, troubled him. The voice called him to leave Haran and journey once more into the unknown. He was destined to be the father of a great nation, the voice told him.

Now this was hard to understand. My husband, not being the first-born son, could not expect especial blessing, also, we had no children. I was barren and Abram had chosen not to take another wife. But my husband believed the voice he heard. Ignoring my protests he gathered together all his wealth, and all his slaves, and we left the comfort of Haran to follow the way of life of a nomad. From that time we have been strangers and pilgrims in every place, having no permanent home, but always searching for the fulfilment of the promise made by the unknown god; and yet we prospered.

Although Abram was called to leave his relatives, Lot and all his household came with us because Abram felt responsible for him. We went south, to the land of Canaan. When we reached Shechem Abram again heard the voice of the unknown god. The promise was renewed and Abram built an altar to the god who had befriended him, calling him the Sovereign Lord.

Since then we have travelled throughout this land; soaked by torrential downpours in winter and parched by arid droughts in summer. We have frozen in the bitter snow-laden winds from Mount Hermon. We have watched the swallows return from Egypt on the spring breezes. Always, the Sovereign Lord has been our guide.

Once famine drove us to Egypt where Pharaoh, believing me to be Abram's sister and not his wife, claimed me for his harem. The Sovereign Lord was angry and punished Pharaoh's house with terrible diseases so that he begged us to leave his land, sending us away with many gifts of atonement. So we continued to prosper, even in adversity. All this time our nephew, Lot, accompanied us until his men squabbled with our men and we parted company.

As I walk to the well beneath the creaking palm trees, the hot sun on my back, I remember all these things. Abram's name is respected in every land as a mighty warrior who loves peace. A man who talks with God. I am a fortunate woman.

There is only one thing lacking. I have no son. I would sacrifice all our fame and wealth, to give my husband a son. There is no joy in riches unless a man has a son to inherit his name; to ensure his memory lives for ever. The Sovereign Lord has promised Abram many times that his descendants will cover the earth as the stars cover the heaven. But how can it be? I have no son. I am barren.

I had a slave girl Hagar, the Egyptian, given to me by Pharaoh. I gave her to my husband so that she could have a son for me. But as soon as she conceived she changed, becoming proud and arrogant; demanding the privileges of a wife, she despised me. When the child was born Abram, overjoyed, gave them a separate household. Now he spends a lot of time there because he loves to spend time with his son, Ishmael.

A year ago, when Ishmael was thirteen years old the Sovereign Lord spoke to my husband again, repeating the promise to make me the mother of many nations. As a sign that he accepted this solemn vow Abram was commanded to see that all our men were circumcised. Also, the Sovereign Lord declared that my husband's name should be changed to Abraham and I was to be known as Sarah. Abraham laughed to think that I, old Sarah, could produce a son. Nevertheless, he obeyed the Sovereign Lord and changed our names and he, and Ishmael, and all our menfolk, were circumcised. Soon after this, just a few months ago, in fact, they had scarcely recovered when the strangers came. Strangers who would change our lives for ever.

In the shade of the palm trees, as I fill the water skins, I recall that curious day . . . Riding on camels, richly dressed, merchants from the North appeared quite suddenly one afternoon. Abraham was dozing at the entrance to his tent. Startled from sleep he clambered to his feet to greet them, calling me to bake the finest bread and hurrying himself to choose and kill the best calf from the flock. It was a splendid feast we prepared for these illustrious guests. When they had eaten and drunk much wine I was listening to their merrymaking at the door of the tent. I heard them promise my husband that the year after their visit I would bear a son. It made me laugh so much that they heard me. They called me, asking why I laughed. I was afraid, so I denied laughing.

And now, looking at the palm trees and listening to the wind in their branches, I remember their words, and my laughter. It is hard to believe but the evidence is clear enough. Something is happening to me. My body is changing. I keep thinking I shall wake up and discover it is a dream. A bad dream. A nightmare. It is hard to accept but it is true. I am pregnant! I wish I had not laughed.

I feel afraid . . . and a bit angry . . . why now? After all this time! It is too late! I am an old woman. I do not want the responsibility. I am set in my ways. I am ready to end my days sitting beside my husband at the door of our tent.

I do not want to face the challenge. I do not want to change. But I shall have to change. It is happening already.

My belly grows fat. New life stirs within me. The pattern of my life is disrupted. I no longer sleep peacefully but vivid dreams disturb me. I wish I had not laughed.

I return from the well with the water skins. The wind rustles in the palm trees. My husband asks what ails me. I cannot answer. I do not know. I cannot explain it to him. He would not understand. I do not understand myself; I should be exhilarated. Has God not promised me a son?

Today my time has come. I am in labour. Skilled midwives are here, summoned by my husband Abraham from the land of Pharaoh to deliver me. They place a wooden gag in my mouth so that my screams will not be heard.

The pain is coming again.
It will not be so bad.
Just a dull ache.
In my back.

I will not think of stories I have heard.
Of women I have known who have died.
I clutch at the midwife.
I fight off the panic.
I will not die.
I must not die.
Pain engulfs
me.
It passes.
Beads of sweat prick my brow.
The women wipe my forehead with a moist cloth,
lavender-scented, and speak soft words to comfort me.

How much longer?
I think the child will never be born.
I am so tired.
I wish I could go to sleep.
Start again tomorrow.
I am so very tired.

I cannot endure much more.
I am too old.
Too tired.
I wish I could just sleep.
Never wake up.
I am so very, very tired.

I hear them whispering.
I cannot hear the words.
I know.
They say I am too old.
They say it is not possible.
They say it is not natural.
They whisper.
I will die.

My old body writhes. It sweats.
It strains. I scream.
And scream.
And scream.
I cry out,
'Where are you,
God of Abraham? Where are you?'

I have no strength left. Now I whisper, 'I should not have laughed. I am sorry I laughed.'

There is stillness in the air like the stillness preceding a storm. Silence. I hear someone panting. It is me. I hear myself screaming. Then, another cry; not a cry of pain; the angry, indignant, baffled wail of new life.

'You have a son,' they say.

Then I hear . . .

laughter
laughter
laughter.

I am laughing. Abraham is laughing. The sound of delighted, unbelieving, joyous laughter is carried on the wind and rings out across the desert. The promise of God

31

is true. I have given birth to a son in my old age. I will be the mother of nations.

## PRAYER

*Sovereign Lord, my journey through life often seems to have no sure direction. The path I tread seems to go round in circles. I fail to see your hand at work in the ordinary circumstances of life. I dare to laugh at your promises. Forgive me. Have mercy on my human frailty.*

*Help me always to keep faith and to recognize and accept you through whatever situation you send to me, however unlikely it may seem.*

*And help me to always be ready to respond to the challenge to change to any new purpose you may have for me, however inadequate I may feel, so that, like Sarah, I may learn to laugh for joy. In Christ's name. Amen.*

### Suggested reading

Genesis 12.1–20; 18.1–15; 21.1–8.

# 4

# THE PRIEST'S MOTHER

*Hannah makes a vow she finds
hard to keep*

—————⋙⋘—————

> The Lord has told us what is good. What he requires of us is
> this: to do what is just, to show constant love, and to live in
> humble fellowship with our God.
>
> (Micah 6.8)

It is late afternoon as we gather for the family meal. The
cooking pot hangs over the fire simmering and steaming
with a delicious aroma of herbs, rosemary, thyme, and
mint. I sit at my husband's feet, gazing into the flames, as
he stirs the portion of the sacrificial bull allowed us by
the law of Moses. This is the time of year for celebration
and feasting. We rose at dawn to pay homage, to offer our
sacrifice and to worship at the temple. Giving thanks for
the harvest we prayed for prosperity and safety in the
coming year. Now we will eat.

I am Hannah, and I come from the hill country of
Ephraim where I live with my husband, Elkanah. Every
year we make our pilgrimage to the temple here at Shiloh
to honour the God of Israel. Elkanah always insists that
his second wife, Peninnah, and her children come with
us. She is a village woman and she lives close to us but in
her own household because her ways are different to ours.

She keeps the gods of the Canaanites in her house and does not obey the law of Moses, saying that the heavens and earth are too much for one god to manage. It grieves my husband, Elkanah.

He is turning the meat over now, looking for the choicest portions. He carefully ladles a generous portion into a dish and passes it to me with a smile. It smells good. Next he gives Peninnah and each of her children a helping of the stew, before serving himself. We give thanks for the food and eat our fill. I feel Peninnah watching me as I begin to eat but I pretend not to notice. Whenever I do look in her direction her eyes are upon me. I am accustomed to her animosity, she is jealous of my close relationship to Elkanah, but today her gaze is unusually malicious.

Before he eats Elkanah leaves us to reassure himself that the animals are safely tethered for the night. As soon as he is out of earshot she leans over and hisses at me, 'Does our husband think to feed you up by giving you a large portion of the finest meat? Does he think you might yet bear him a son? You would do better to mix the root of the mandrake with your fodder.' She pauses to smile at her children, then she leers at me and continues, 'Perhaps he thinks to console you. I'm afraid you're more likely to grow fat and sluggish, the way he lavishes extra portions on you. Never mind. I can have his sons for him. Look at my children; so strong and healthy! Our husband has been blessed through me. His name will be remembered in the city gate because I have borne him a son. But you, Hannah, Elkanah's God has forsaken you! You pray to him but he doesn't hear.' She sneers again and covers her ears, 'Perhaps you should call him louder, or' she covers her open mouth with her hand, as if shocked, then whispers, 'perhaps you have sinned, Hannah. Do you have some secret sin which causes you to be barren?' Then she laughs outright, a harsh and mirthless sound, 'I think you should appeal to Asherah, the wife of Baal, as I have done. Make cakes for her and pour out a drink offering to her. She might hear you and give you the son which the God of Elkanah has refused you!'

Peninnah is silenced by Elkanah's return. I bite my lip and finger my food. Every year it's the same. She insults me and taunts me. This year her mockery is worse than ever. I feel I can't endure it any longer.

And why? Why does the Lord God punish me? Have I offended the God of Abraham? Is he angry with me? I have lived a blameless life, keeping the law of Moses since I was a girl. Can it be true? Should I sacrifice to the Canaanite gods? Would they hear me?

My husband interrupts my thoughts, 'You're not eating,' he says. 'What's wrong with you? Are you sick?' There is concern in his voice but also some displeasure. I'm unable to answer.

'Hannah, why aren't you eating?'

I look at him and try to smile, 'I'm sorry. I'm tired. The ceremony in the temple has wearied me.'

He frowns but says nothing. To please him I take a morsel of bread, dip it in my dish, and putting it into my mouth, I try to chew. My mouth is dry. The food tastes like sand. I try to swallow and it sticks in my throat. Coughing and spluttering I hastily excuse myself from the table and hurry outside. I want to be alone but Elkanah follows me.

'What is it, Hannah? Why are you so unhappy? I don't understand. You used to enjoy our visits to the temple to celebrate the harvest. What's happened to you?'

It's difficult to answer him, 'It's because . . . I wish I could . . .' I can hardly get the words out, 'I haven't given you a son, Elkanah.' It sounds like an accusation.

'A son!' He is genuinely astonished. 'I thought you'd got over that years ago! I have a son, Peninnah's child. Why are you worrying about it now?' He is shocked, but he puts his arms around me and draws me close. 'My dear,' he says tenderly, 'don't you know you are more precious to me than ten sons?'

I start to cry. When I have quietened down he says, 'Hannah, I love you. It's true I took Peninnah as my wife so that I could have a son. It's true. But you are worth more, much more, than a son to me.'

'You don't understand, Elkanah,' I sniff, 'I'm glad you have a son. Glad Peninnah has given you many children. But can't you understand my disgrace? The shame I feel. Don't you know how people wag their tongues at me? . . . and,' I hesitate, 'Peninnah, too.'

'Peninnah?'

'Yes. She taunts me. When you're not listening. She says . . . ,' but I find I can't tell him any more. He holds me close for a while then says,

'Well, having a son is no guarantee of happiness. Eli the priest has two sons to gladden his heart, Hophni and Phinehas, but everyone knows how they defile the name of the Lord and disgrace their father. Better to have no son than to have sons like them to break my heart.'

I am not listening to him. 'If only the Lord God would give me a son I would be content. I would not complain any more but I would dedicate him to the Lord for as long as he lived.'

'Since it matters so much to you, why don't you go to the temple now and make a special petition to the Lord God? Perhaps he will hear you. Go now. Tomorrow we journey home. Wait! I will come with you.'

'No, Elkanah. Thank you. I will go but I must do this alone.'

I leave my husband, cover my head, and hurry to the temple gate. The rays of the setting sun glow red on the walls of the sacred place, the air is heavy with frankincense. In the shadow of the doorway the old priest, Eli, sits watching the people come and go. As I enter he smiles benevolently at me and I bow in deference, as do the other worshippers who pass by. He sits very still, his attention absorbed by the passing crowds.

I approach as close to the Ark of the Covenant as the

law permits, and bend down low to the ground. I search my mind for suitable words to address the Lord God, the Holy One. None of the temple chants or songs seem appropriate. I do not know what I should say. I lift my hands and whisper the thoughts that come from my heart, 'O Lord my God, I do not know who you are. I do not know how I should speak to you. But, I believe you are the God of Abraham who gave Sarah a son when she was old. You are the God of Moses who heard his mother's cry and spared her baby from the slaughter. Hear my prayer. Let my cry come unto you. You are holy and righteous and I am only a poor woman. You were pleased to hear the prayer of your servant Deborah and gave her victory over her enemies. Hear my prayer. Let my cry come unto you. You have heard how my rival mocks your name. Give me a son, I beseech you, that she may know that you are greater than the gods of this land. Holy Lord, hear my prayer. I have no sacrifice to offer you, but if you will hear my prayer, if you will give me a son, I will return him to you. Give me a son and I swear that he will be a Nazarite, dedicated to your service as long as he lives. His hair will not be cut nor his face shaved all the days of his life but he will serve you here, in this your temple. Hear my prayer. Take away my disgrace. Give me a son, I beseech you.'

As I pray I wipe away my tears with my hair. I hear nothing. I see nothing.

'Woman!'

The voice startles me. A stern voice. For a moment I don't know where I am. I lift my head a little. My eyes catch sight of a blue hem embroidered with pomegranates and decorated with tiny silver bells, just inches from my face. The bells chime softly as the wearer of the beautiful garment moves. It is the priest. He stands over me where I am crouching.

'Woman!' Now I look up. In the flickering light of the temple lamps the priest is scowling angrily at me.

'Sir?' my voice trembles.

'What are you doing here in such a state? I've been watching you, beating your chest and tugging your hair out. I've seen your lips moving without speech. How dare you defile this holy place with your drunkenness. You should be ashamed of yourself. Get up and go home to your husband.'

'Sir?' in the shadows his portly frame is awesome. I'm at a loss to understand his anger. I become aware that my hair is hanging down around my face. My head is uncovered, my clothes dishevelled, from the agony of my praying. Nervously I push my hair back from my face and slowly raise my eyes to his, while covering my head with my shawl.

'No! No, sir! Excuse me for speaking but certainly I haven't been drinking! Not at all! I'm in despair. I've come here to make my petition to the Lord God Almighty.'

'You've come here, alone, to pray?'

'Yes, sir.'

He looks at me, keenly, and my heart falters in the intensity of his gaze. Then he says, 'Tell me your story. Who are you and where do you come from?'

'My name is Hannah and I have come with my husband Elkanah from the town of Ramah.'

'Ramah? A day's journey south?'

'Yes, sir. He is a wealthy man and he lives by the law and has nothing to do with the pagan gods. We come here every year to present our first fruits to the Lord God.' I pause before adding, 'I am his first wife.'

'His first wife?'

'Yes, sir. Our marriage was arranged when we were very young but over the years we have grown to love each other very much.'

And I go on to tell him my sorrow, not only in being childless, but also because Peninnah is so unkind to me. While I speak, Eli the priest gazes out at the distant hills where the sun is dropping below the horizon. When I have finished my story he leans towards me and asks gently, 'You have been married for many years?'

'Yes, sir. Under the law my husband is entitled to divorce me but he chose instead to take another wife. To spare my feelings he established her household a short distance from ours. But each year when we come to celebrate the festival of ingathering, she lives with us, and she taunts me.'

'And you are not content to accept things as they are? You cannot be at peace, believing that the Lord God does all things well?'

'Oh, sir, I might well be content. I am skilled in the crafts of weaving and embroidery. I make many garments and each year when we come to worship and offer sacrifices here at Shiloh I bring garments for the priests and ornaments for the temple. I could be content. I used to look forward to coming. It was the highlight of my life. The journey is long and tiresome but I love the festivities, the dancing and feasting.'

'But now you feel differently?'

'Yes, because at every opportunity she insults me. I can't bear it. She tells me to offer sacrifices to the gods of this land.'

I stop speaking, clasping and unclasping my hands; wringing them as if I were doing the laundry at the washing place. I can't keep them still.

The priest doesn't speak for several minutes. Finally, he says, 'Go in peace. May the God of Israel give you what you have asked him for. I will offer a sacrifice for you.'

'May you always think kindly of me,' I reply and take my leave. Suddenly I feel much better, as if a great weight has been lifted from me. I feel calmer. I feel at peace. And, I feel hungry. Elkanah is astonished when I return to our tent and start to eat the food which is still simmering in the pot.

Four years have passed. Bittersweet years. I am again at the temple in Shiloh with my husband Elkanah. Peninnah is not with us.

Barely nine months after my last, lonely, visit to the temple, the Lord heard my prayer and gave me a son. A fine, healthy child. I had a difficult pregnancy with sickness and headaches and swollen limbs. I felt ill the whole time. Then, when I went into labour the baby was born quickly but I was ill for weeks afterwards. Elkanah was afraid I would die. Although I was so sick I rejoiced to have a son. I called the boy Samuel, which means, God has heard me.

And God was good. I recovered. I nursed my baby with great joy. I could hardly believe the miracle of his birth but all the while I thanked the God of Abraham and Sarah I remembered my vow. It weighed heavily on me.

The year after his birth I told Elkanah that I was not well enough to travel to Shiloh with him. The following year Samuel had a cold and he was not fit to make the journey. And the next year I found another reason for remaining at home. I could not bring myself to face up to the vow I had made. The child was too young, too precious. When he took his first faltering steps, a look of deep concentration on his face, he looked up at me and beamed. Bump, he fell over, and looked surprised. Then he was hauling himself up, tugging at my skirt, to try again. When he spoke his first words, we celebrated with all our neighbours and he threw his head back and laughed aloud with delight. Although I had longed for a child I never knew, never imagined, such joy was possible. I could not part with him. Surely the Lord did not require this sacrifice? In my heart of hearts, I knew he did; but not yet. Not until the child was weaned. Each day was so precious to me.

So I stopped making the pilgrimage to Shiloh, waiting until my son was old enough to go to the temple. Peninnah made excuses to remain at Ramah, too. So Elkanah made the journey to sacrifice alone. I knew he was saddened by this but he understood my reluctance and Peninnah's unwillingness had always been clear to him. It no longer surprised him.

This year, however, after much heart-searching, and with Elkanah's encouragement, I have come. We brought a bull with us for our sacrifice, and this morning we made our offering. This evening we are sitting, with our son, to eat together. We sit and eat in silence, with heavy hearts. In the morning we will go to see the priest . . .

The day dawned bright and clear. We have come to the temple. The priest is approaching now, the bells on his tunic chiming as I remember them on my last visit. Elkanah gives me a little push and I step forward.

'Excuse me, sir. Do you remember me?'

Eli, the priest, looks keenly into my eyes. Then he glances towards Elkanah, who is holding Samuel in his arms.

'Yes,' the old man says slowly. 'I do remember you. I thought you were intoxicated.'

'Yes sir, you did,' I answer. 'I was praying to the Lord for a son.'

'I remember,' he says.

Turning to Elkanah, who is holding Samuel in his arms, I say, 'This is my husband, and this our child. The Lord heard my cry and answered me. Now,' I hesitate, 'and now . . .' I open my mouth to speak but no words come. I try to continue. I have lost my voice. I feel Elkanah's hand laid gently on my shoulder. I take a deep breath, clear my throat and try again. 'Now I have come to fulfil my promise to the Lord. I vowed that if he answered my prayer and gave me a son the child would be a Nazarite, dedicated to serve the Lord all the days of his life. He is now almost four years old and his hair has not been cut to show that he belongs to the Lord. He has been fully weaned. Now, he is yours, so that you may teach him and instruct him in the ways of the Lord.' The words tumble out in a rush. I must speak quickly. I must make my declaration public before I can change my mind. 'Take him, sir,' I say, grabbing my son from Elkanah's arms and thrusting him into the arms of the old priest. Tears are streaming down my face. I feel my heart will break.

Samuel says, 'Mother, why are you crying?'

Through my tears I smile at my son trying desperately to keep my voice steady, I say, 'You are going to live here in this great temple, to serve the Lord God. This is a very special thing for you to do and I am very proud of you . . . but I shall miss you, Samuel. You will live here with the priest. I shall come every year to see you, and I will make you a special tunic, like the priest's garment, and bring it for you.'

My little son turns to study the priest's robe, running his tiny fingers over the blue and gold embroidered pomegranates, then, hesitantly shaking the tiny bells to hear them ring.

'Will I have bells that ring?'

'Yes. I will make some tiny ones for you.'

'And pretty patterns too?'

'Yes. I will embroider your tunic. It will be just like the priest's tunic, but small enough to fit you.'

Samuel's face beams up at me. 'Ooh! I shall like that. When shall I have it?'

Fighting back my tears I pick him up and hug him hard. I kiss his curly head; his eyes; his soft rosy cheeks; his tiny mouth. Then I hand my son over to the priest.

Eli, now holding Samuel in his arms, blesses Elkanah and me, and says, 'Because you have done this thing and kept your vow, the Lord will bless you and give you other children to take the place of this one whom you have dedicated to the Lord.'

Then Eli lowers Samuel to the floor saying, 'It is a very wonderful thing your Mother and Father are doing, Samuel, dedicating you to the Lord God. You will live here in the temple with me and learn how to be a priest like me. Do you think you'll like that?'

'Can I light the lamps?' Samuel asks, with shining eyes.

'Yes, in time, you can light the lamps,' Eli answers, with a laugh.

I watch the old man and my little son toddle off together, hand in hand. Samuel doesn't give me a second glance. I feel a pang of hurt, and anxiety. Will my child fret? Will he be homesick? Have I done the right thing? I want to rush after them. I want to cry out, 'Come back. Come back. I've made a mistake. I've changed my mind. He's not old enough yet.'

I start forward. Elkanah holds me. I am rooted to the spot but in spite of myself my heart is singing. How strange it is. The words that come into my heart are words of victory; words of joy: 'My heart rejoices in the Lord, in the Lord my horn is lifted high. My mouth boasts over my enemies, for I delight in your deliverance.'

Elkanah's arms are strong around me. Somehow I know that everything is going to be alright.

'We will see him next year,' he says.

'Yes,' I answer, 'and how he will have grown. As soon as we get home I shall start weaving to make him a new tunic. I'll embroider it with tiny pomegranates, and with silver bells, like the priest's bells. I shall enjoy doing that, and we can bring it with us when we come to worship next year.'

'Yes,' Elkanah answers, and arm in arm we make our way back through the moonlight to our dwelling. Tomorrow we leave for Ramah.

PRAYER

*Lord Christ, you know what it is to be laughed at and misunderstood. You know how much it hurts. Help me not to be quick to judge others. Help me to understand the difference between laughing with, and laughing at, people. Give me the courage to refrain from joining in with those who ridicule others.*

*May I be strong, patient and kind when others mock*

*me. Help me to keep faith with you in good as well as bad times knowing there are no easy answers. May I, like Job, bless your name, knowing that the Lord gives and the Lord takes away. Hear me, Lord, who had all and who was ready to lose all, in order that I might live. Amen.*

*Suggested reading*

1 Samuel 1.1–28.

# 5

# THE KING'S MISTRESS

*A story of infidelity, treachery
and forgiveness*

--------⌒⌒⌒⌒◉⌒⌒⌒⌒--------

Jesus said to them, 'Whichever one of you has committed no
sin may throw the first stone at her.'

(John 8.7)

Neither of us mentions the fear. It hangs between us like
a curtain. David holds our baby level with his eyes, sitting
him on one hand and supporting his head with the other,
and I watch in silence as they regard one another. The
mighty warrior king and the newborn child; my husband
and my son; all our past and all our future suspended in
this moment. I hold my breath, not daring to speak.
Tomorrow is the eighth day and Nathan the prophet will
come to circumcise and name the child. It is exactly a year
ago today since our first son died; seven days old, and we
never named him. We do not speak of it. It is as though he
never existed.

There is just the three of us. We dismissed the servants,
wanting to be alone for this first meeting. I look at my
husband. He is still such an enigma to me; handsome,
strong and decisive, he commands the devotion of his
subjects and the respect of his enemies. But with me he is
as gentle and tender as any shepherd boy might be. He is

a dreamer, a poet. No-one would believe how he agonizes over issues of state; how he wrestles with his conscience about private temptations and weaknesses of the flesh. I saw those contradictions most clearly when our first child was born, and died . . . the tragedy about which we dare not speak.

'He is so small. Is he strong?' I am jolted out of my musing by David's level voice, but the fear is in the question. Will it happen again? Could the Lord the Eternal be so cruel? . . . Surely not.

'He is strong,' it is hard not to sound afraid.

David glances at me. We avoid each other's eyes. The other child was sickly from the moment of his birth, and things are different this time. We are married now. What we did was wrong and the Lord, the Eternal punished us. Will he punish us forever?

My husband is studying our son again.

'He is so small,' he says, 'I had forgotten how small they are. So vulnerable,' then, more cheerfully, 'just look at those tiny hands. So perfect. Look at the minute finger nails, each one completely formed. And his little pink mouth, like a hungry sparrow. Oh, look he is yawning,' and David laughs with delight.

I laugh too, with joy and relief. I move closer. 'Yes, and look at those enormous eyelashes.'

'He is beautiful,' David says, his voice gruff with emotion.

'He has got a handsome father.'

'To say nothing of his beautiful mother.'

'We are a beautiful couple, aren't we?' I speak lightly, with a smile, trying to push away the shadow of shame, which hangs over us. Trying to ignore the anxiety.

'Look. Look at his long fingers. Perhaps he will grow up to play the harp, like you.' In spite of myself my words carry a hint of reproach. David knows it. He has not touched his music for many months.

'Tonight I shall play and sing for you . . . For both of you.'

'And for his brother?'

'Yes. For his brother, too.'

I am relieved. I feel tears pricking my eyes but I dare not show them. This is the first time the child's death has been acknowledged, it is the nearest we can get to discussing it.

To hide my hurt I ask, 'What shall he be called?' This time I manage to keep my voice steady. There is a long pause before David says, almost defiantly, 'He will be called Solomon.'

'Solomon.' I repeat the name, carefully. 'Peace?'

'Yes, Solomon. The Eternal has blessed us with another son. He has forgiven us. This is a new start for us, Bathsheba.'

Almost, I think I believe it. Can we really put the past behind us and start again? Does the Lord, the Eternal really forgive? I cast my mind back . . .

It is barely two years but it seems much longer. I was married to another man then, Uriah, a commander in the King's army. A Hittite. We had been married for several years but there was no joy in our relationship. It was not that there was anything wrong, exactly. Uriah was a good man. Too good perhaps. It might have been different if we had been blessed with children, but we had none.

Uriah had been at court the very first time I was asked to entertain the King's guests. My father arranged it because he liked to show me off. I did not mind. I had worked hard with my teacher, studying the intricate movements of traditional dancing and I was good at it. I liked nothing better than to show off my expertise to an appreciative audience. I liked the applause, and the rewards that it brought me, too.

I had often danced for my father's guests and I was always very well received. My hair is my best feature. It is splendid; waist-length, auburn-coloured and it cascades down my back in a shower of curls. Orpah says it is very beautiful; and when I dance I toss it like a veil over my face. Orpah is my maid, a gift from my father on my twelfth birthday. She is Egyptian, and as dark as I am fair. She tells me my skin is as delicate as a mountain lily, but I dare say she exaggerates! Certainly, I have fine bones and an unusually light complexion.

Although I was accustomed to entertaining I can still remember my excitement when I was invited to dance for the King. I was too nervous to eat for days. Orpah was almost as delighted as me. We spent hours choosing the right gown and she went to great lengths to oil and arrange my hair, and to accentuate my eyes more than usual with the finest kohl available. She said I looked lovelier than ever; and by the time she'd finished grooming me I looked and smelt like an Egyptian princess; I was dripping with perfume.

When the evening finally arrived I was so apprehensive I felt sick. But as soon as the musicians started to play I forgot my fear; my feet seemed to carry me away; I felt my body swaying and twisting to the music like the strings of a harp. My gown swirled round me in a haze of colour shimmering and gleaming in the light of the lanterns. I forgot I was being watched and just let the rhythm of the drums become part of me. Quicker and quicker the music went and my feet flew on air; I twirled and twisted, whirled and spun, swifter, swifter; leaping and pirouetting faster and faster, tossing my head, weaving and coiling my arms until I was dizzy. I was exhilarated. I was in another world. Then it was over.

In the evening, as she prepared me for bed, Orpah said, 'You pleased the King with your dancing tonight.' It is funny she should have said that. I remember it because of the look on her face. It was the first time I had seen it, faraway and thoughtful. I have seen it often since. But that was the first time.

A few days after the banquet my father came to see me.

'Uriah the Hittite was impressed with your dancing, Bathsheba.'

'I danced well, didn't I? Were you pleased with me?'

'Of course, very pleased. I was proud of you, as I always am.'

'What will you give me as a reward?'

He laughed, as he always did. 'You are so like your mother sometimes! What would you like?'

'What can I have?'

He laughed again, 'What about a dowry?'

'A dowry?' I was amazed. After a long time I said, 'Who?'

'Guess.'

I was not sure I wanted to guess. Of course, I knew that the matter of my marriage must come up sooner or later, but this was even sooner than I had expected. It was rather a shock, although I was 12 years old and might have known my father would be making plans. To cover my confusion I asked, 'Is it someone I know?'

'It is someone you've met. Someone who enjoyed your dancing.'

'Oh, that's no clue. Everyone enjoys my dancing. That's why you suggested it. You know it is.' I pouted at him. 'Do not tease me Father. Tell me who. Is he rich? Is he handsome? Tell me!'

'Uriah has asked for your hand.'

'Uriah?! Uriah the Hittite?! But he is a foreigner! And he is . . . old!'

'He is rich and powerful. You will be an important lady.'

'But, Father!'

'Come now, child . . . Think about it. You will be married to a man who is second in command in the King's army. You will be welcome and have influence in court circles . . .'

'Ah, so that's it. If I marry Uriah, you and grandfather will have influence at court. I see it now.'

'I am not going to force you, Bathsheba. I want you to be happy, but I want you to think about it. There are many advantages you know. It is a great honour that such an important man has asked to marry you. Besides, have you really looked at him? He is quite handsome . . . And he will know how to keep you in hand.'

'Whatever do you mean? Keep me in hand?'

'You're very pretty and you're not above a little flirtation. You need a husband who will be tolerant of your high spirits, but who will know how to keep your lovers at bay.'

'When I am married I shan't have any lovers, Father.'

'I wonder,' he said, and laughed again. 'I shouldn't want to be responsible for you for too long, my child.'

'Whatever do you mean?' I protested. But he just went off, laughing.

I asked Orpah what he meant when she was brushing my hair that evening.

'He means you are lively and fleet-footed as a gazelle, and just as heedless of danger. Your dancing will lead you astray if you are not careful. But you need not worry; I will watch out for you, my lady.' And she smiled her secret smile again. An expression I have come to know so well, though it puzzles me. It often seems that Orpah knows more than she is telling and sometimes I even think she has magic Egyptian powers because, although I am her mistress, it sometimes seems as if she is the one in control. It is foolish to think so. She is, after all, only a slave.

Father thought he was doing well for me, settling my marriage to Uriah. I didn't mind. I had to marry someone and it was true, the general was eminently eligible; a man of some significance and quite good-looking in his own way; rich, powerful and greatly respected. I came to admire him very much. Actually, I was a little bit afraid of him. As his wife I was treated with considerable deference in spite of my youth. I was very proud, at first, of my position. But marriage to Uriah was rather stifling. Although he was a Hittite he kept every detail of the law more assiduously than many of my countrymen, never deviating to the slightest degree. Everything was so serious. So correct. Even in bed. He had no sense of fun, no sense of humour. To be honest, he was a little dull.

It might not have mattered. I enjoyed my life and we were frequently at court where I often entertained the King's guests with my dancing. I loved it. So did Uriah, who was as pleased and proud of me as my Father had been.

I was aware that I interested the King. I pretended not to notice. But secretly I found it thrilling to know that he was watching me. On feast days as I sat laughing beside my husband, I felt the King's eyes on me. When I glanced in his direction he looked away, but I knew. It became an obsession. When I danced, I danced for the King. When I sang, I sang for the King. I would lie awake and think of him. When I slept, I dreamt of him. Even when I was in bed with Uriah I imagined myself in the King's arms.

It is shocking, I know. Perhaps I shouldn't speak of these things. The attraction I felt for the King was terribly disturbing. Every time I heard his name my heart fluttered, my hands started sweating and I felt myself blushing. I was convinced it was obvious to everyone but no-one commented. It might not have mattered, of course, if he had not noticed me. But he had. And I knew he had. It was driving me mad. I confided in Orpah, because I had to tell someone, but she was not surprised. In fact she understood the situation better than I did.

'It is fate,' she said knowingly, 'it is meant to be.'

'After all,' I recall her words, 'you are only human. No-one can change destiny. Princess or slave, the gods decide our fate. It is not in our hands.' Then she said, 'It is the custom amongst my people to seek guidance at the shrine of the goddess Maat. Would you like me to go and make sacrifices to the oracle on your behalf, my lady?'

I did not answer her. I did not know then and I do not know now how much we control our own future by the choices we make. Perhaps she is right and everything is foreordained? Perhaps the gods do use us as playthings for their amusement as Orpah believes; but Nathan, the prophet of Israel, tells us to worship only the one true god who is called the Eternal. It is all very strange.

As far as I know, Orpah didn't go to the shrine for me, but I felt troubled. It was as if I were a bee trapped in a bowl of honey; sweet and satisfying at first, but then inescapable and deadly. Maybe what followed was wrong or even wicked, but it was out of my control, and perhaps it was necessary. I can't truthfully say I have any regrets. I wouldn't change anything now even if I could. It is too difficult for me to understand; it happened, that is all. It is for others to understand.

Of course, if Uriah had been aware of what was going on things might have turned out differently. But he was oblivious. He adored me and as far as he was concerned, I could do no wrong; it is strange that men are so easily taken in by a pretty face. Anyway, even if Uriah had noticed my flirtation with King David he would have been flattered, not concerned. It was well known that the King admired beautiful women. Uriah was devoted to the King and immensely loyal, he would have been honoured to have his wife admired. Besides, I know Uriah would never have been unfaithful to me so he could never imagine that I might deceive him. I would not have believed it of myself, for that matter.

Orpah had an admirer in the court. She said to me one day, 'I hear the King wants you, my lady.'

'Whatever do you mean, wants me?'

'You know what I mean,' she said.

I blushed with shame, 'How dare you say so!'

'Forgive me, my lady, but I am acquainted with one of his manservants and it is well known that he desires you.'

I was silent, thinking about it. I was flattered, naturally, but I couldn't show it, not even to Orpah.

'Be careful with my hair,' I said. 'You're hurting me.'

For a while nothing happened and life continued as

before. I could have believed it was all a mistake, the whimsy of a young girl. Our love might have flourished and withered without consummation, had it not been for Orpah . . . and that last campaign.

To this day, I do not know if David planned it. I dare not ask. I only know that Uriah my husband was summoned along with his men to march against Rabbah. Joab was in command and Uriah was his right-hand man. They laid siege to the city while David remained in the palace. It was spring, I remember, when the lilies were in full bloom. Their scent filled the city. And it was hot, so hot.

David was alone in his palace. And I was alone in my villa. Many long, lonely days passed. Hot, sultry days. Time hung on my hands while I sat motionless at my embroidery, hour after hour, thinking about David, wondering what he was doing . . . Wondering if he was thinking about me. I tried to work, but my fingers were clumsy and heavy. At night I lay awake, smelling the heady scent of lilies and yearning for him.

Early one evening Orpah came to me, 'It is so hot,' she said, 'I have prepared a bath for you in the garden, where it is cooler.'

It was a lovely idea. The air was fragrant with jasmine and I luxuriated in the caress of the fresh water running over my skin. Orpah oiled my body with sweet-smelling spikenard then, as she was massaging my feet she whispered, 'Do not look now, but we are being watched,' and she bent over my feet and calmly continued with her task.

I was appalled, but she continued to stroke my feet gently and I saw she was smiling.

'Orpah, I do not understand! What do you mean?'

She whispered that she had noticed the King walking on the palace roof, not once but many times, late in the afternoon. He had been there, often, silhouetted against the sky as the sun was setting.

She smiled her secret smile, 'Why do you think he walks there, my lady? He has cool gardens, fragrant with honeysuckle, and beautiful women in his harem to keep him company.'

I felt myself burning with shame. With shame . . . and, yes, . . . with longing.

Not many days after this a messenger came secretly from the palace and took me to the King. To David . . . We became lovers . . . I conceived his child . . .

It was a shock to discover I was pregnant. In all the years I had been married to Uriah it had not happened. I had almost resigned myself to remaining barren. The possibility of carrying David's child had not entered my head. At first I did not know what to do but Orpah insisted that I should tell the King. She said it was essential.

I was very fearful when I told David, not knowing how he would react; nor could I have guessed what his reaction would be. It was a mixture of disbelief, joy and alarm.

He told me to return to my home, assuring me that he would find some way of dealing with the situation. I learnt later that he sent at once to Joab demanding news of the siege. He commanded that my husband should be sent home immediately to give Joab's report directly to the King himself. When Uriah had delivered his brief, my husband was given leave to visit me.

It was the obvious thing to do. Such a good idea. Uriah would believe the child to be his and he would be over-joyed. I prepared myself, with Orpah's assistance, and awaited his arrival. But he didn't come. Uriah confounded the King by refusing to visit me because he said he could not spend time relaxing and enjoying himself whilst his men were in danger. I was dumbstruck! I felt so insulted! How could he put concern for his men above his regard for me? Much later I discovered the affront was even greater than I had thought. Orpah told me she heard that David had plied Uriah with drink, certain that this would lend success to his plan. But Uriah was adamant; he would not relax while his men were in danger. As I have said, he was a truly upright man.

But what to do? It was an impossible situation. Orpah obtained news and brought it to me that David was exasperated. I was angry and frustrated. What could we do? What would happen? I fretted about it for days in spite of Orpah's assurances that I should not worry.

'Be still, my lady. King David is a wise man. He will think of something,' she said.

Soon after this my husband Uriah called on me briefly to tell me he was returning to his place with his men at the siege. When he had gone, King David sent for me. Taking me in his arms he assured me I need no longer worry.

'I do not understand you, my Lord. My husband did not come to my bed and when the child is born he will know I have been unfaithful to him,' my voice trembled.

'The enemy is strong and cunning. It may be that there will be a battle. The life of a soldier is not without risk,' he said.

'What do you mean?'

'I called you here to tell you there is no need to worry. I am confident that everything will work out for the best for all of us.'

'But how? How can it? How can you know?'

'I do know. I want you to go back to your villa now. Your servant Orpah will take care of you. Before the baby is born our problems will be resolved. I am confident of it. You must trust me, Bathsheba.'

The King spoke so confidently that my fears vanished. I was not sure what he meant. I did not want to think about the implication in his words. The King, my lover was very calm; a good man, favoured by the Eternal, why should I not trust him?

Uriah had not been back with the army very long before a messenger came, post haste, to say that there had been a terrible battle. My husband had been in the front line. He had been killed. He had died a hero's death. I found no comfort in that. In spite of everything, the news of his death was a terrible shock. I loved David, but Uriah was my husband. I had been little more than a child when we married, and he had been good to me; the sense of loss was overwhelming. Even though every soldier's wife lives on a knife edge knowing that sudden death may strike, bereavement, when it comes, is always unexpected. I regretted, more than ever, Uriah's absence on his last visit to the palace, and not just because of the baby. There were so many things I wish I had been able to say to him. I wish I had been able to thank him for all his kindnesses to me. I wish I had been able to say goodbye to him, to tell him that I loved him in my own way. I wished I had been able to ask for his forgiveness.

I mourned the death of Uriah, the Hittite, my husband. For many days I did not see or hear from David. It seemed he had grown tired of me. I was wretched. I felt completely abandoned.

'No, my lady. It wouldn't be right for the King to send for you while you are in mourning. Be calm. Be patient,' Orpah said, trying to console me. She was right, of course, as she always is. When a suitable period had elapsed to satisfy convention, David sent for me. He took me in his arms and kissed me. Then he invited me to join his household as his wife. It was more than I dared to hope for and I was overjoyed.

Our joy was short-lived. Nathan the prophet visited David and I do not know what he said but David was very solemn afterwards. When our son was born he was sickly. David refused to eat and he refused to see anyone. He refused to see me. I was distraught. Our child survived for just seven days. I can barely recall those days. I was too ill to understand what was happening. But Orpah cared for me, I remember that.

It is barely two years but it seems much longer. I have been in a dark place, but no more . . .

Today is the eighth day. I sit at my window in my sumptuous apartments in the palace, right next door to the King's quarters, watching the evening sun set behind the western hills. The sky is mellow with a rose-red light. My baby is sleeping peacefully, cradled in my arms.

It has been a wonderful day. Nathan the prophet came and circumcised our infant son, naming him Jedidiah which means beloved of the Lord. I thought that was rather wonderful; but we still call him Solomon. The prophet, a wise man who understands many things, spent a long time with me. He promised to be my friend because he said my son will inherit David's throne. I do not understand how that may be because David has other sons but Nathan assures me it will be so. He says Solomon will be a great king, a wise king, whose name will live forever. Generations to come will honour him and wherever men speak of justice they will remember my child, Solomon.

I cradle my little son in my arms. He is so tiny. I hold him close, watching the long lashes brush his cheeks as he suckles at my breast. I do not see the future King of Israel. I see my infant son; the son of David; beloved of the Lord.

### PRAYER

*Father in heaven, I make mistakes. Sometimes deliberately, sometimes because I can't help myself, sometimes because I am ignorant of the full implications of what I do.*

*I thank you that you know me better than I know myself; and that your mercy is always greater than my need.*

*Have mercy on me and help me to walk with ever growing awareness and confidence in the paths of love and truth. When I fail, give me grace to forgive myself so that I may be more able to forgive others. Amen.*

*Suggested reading*

2 Samuel 11.1–26; 12.1–25.

# 6

# KINDNESS IN ADVERSITY

*A widow shows a stranger kindness
and finds faith*

---

I tell you that this poor widow put more in the offering box
than all the others. For the others put in what they had to
spare . . . but she . . . gave all she had to live on.

(Mark 12.43–44)

Death is not such a terrible thing. They say it is just like
falling asleep. It is an end to all this suffering. I cannot
fight any more. If there is a God in heaven he will understand. I just cannot go on living like this but I shall see that
we die well, my son and I.

The land is desolate. For three years we have not had
rain, not felt its cleansing power, nor breathed its refresh-
ing fragrance. The skies thunder but no rain falls. The
rivers run dry. The fields are parched, brown and wrinkled.
There is no grain in the store houses. The cattle are dying.
Ships from distant lands no longer visit our port, we have
nothing to trade. Even the rich go hungry. It is said that
Elijah, the prophet of Israel, has cursed the land.

I sit on the beach, here at Zarephath, looking out to
the distant horizon, where the sea touches the sky, and
remember. I would sit here with my husband, watching
the boats come and go, oars dipping in the water, sails

billowing in the wind. It was our favourite place. Now he is dead. He took the donkeys to a distant well to fetch water. On the way back he fell into the hands of brigands, who killed him, robbed him and seized our mules. Now we are alone, my son and I. Soon we shall die too.

I am not afraid. It will be a happy release but I do feel sad for my son. He is the only one of my babies to survive his first birthday, all the others died, and he is still so young. We had high hopes for him, his father and I. We wanted him to have a better life than ours. It does seem so unfair. It might have been different if his father had lived. He would have known what to do now, he always knew what to do. Life can be so unfair and very difficult at times. Some people have an easy existence enjoying abundance, while others always have to struggle with so little to show for it.

But this is no time for regrets. I must take heart and not allow my son see me grieve. All flesh is grass and God will be with us as we set out on the dark journey before us. We will sleep the sleep of death, but first we will satisfy ourselves by eating the very best bread I can bake, and we will strengthen our spirits by feasting our eyes upon the beauty of this world. I have just enough flour and oil to make a fine loaf. It will be our last. I will go to the dry stream bed to collect bulrushes, and sea lavender, too. I will decorate the house. If we must die it will be a good death. My home will be beautiful and my son will die in my arms.

While my child sleeps I have come to search for firewood, just enough to light the oven. It may be our last meal but I will make it a banquet to remember.

It is unbearably hot! The sun has just risen, already it scorches the ground. My feet are burning on the stones. Hot stones, dry earth, but very little kindling. Perhaps over there, behind those rocks I might find some.

I see a stranger. A foreigner. He looks worn out. Exhausted. Dressed in the hair tunic and leather girdle of a prophet, but so unkempt. Can he really be a prophet? He has clearly travelled a long way. I wonder where he is from and where he is going. It does not look as if he can go much farther. I feel sorry for him. He looks half dead. Poor man. He has seen me staring at him. He is beckoning to me. I will go to him.

'Please bring me a drink of water, and some bread,' he says.

'By the living God, I swear that I have not got any bread,' I answer, but I give him water from my water skin. He drinks thirstily.

'All I have is a handful of flour in a bowl and a drop of olive oil in a jar,' I tell him, and explain that I am to cook a last meal for my son and myself.

'Do not worry,' he answers. 'Go ahead and prepare your meal. But first make a small loaf from what you have and bring it to me, and then prepare the rest for you and your son. You will have more tomorrow, I promise you.'

I smile at the absurdity of this, 'He is delirious, his words are the ramblings of a dying man,' I think to myself but I say, 'Of course you must share our bread, sir. And I have an upper room where you can rest and recover.'

I do not expect him to recover but it is no great sacrifice to do as he requests and share our last meal with him. I cannot refuse him. His need is as great as ours. It is no great sacrifice for us to have a little less in order that he may share what little we have. It is the right thing to do. He shall end his days in whatever comfort I can offer.

A fine meal it is. Using every grain of flour and every drop of oil, filling the house with the fragrance of sea lavender, I excel myself. It is indeed a banquet to remember. The next day my guest, very much recovered, asks me for bread. I say I have none.

'Look in your jar,' he says.

'It is empty, sir,' I answer.

'Go and look,' he says.

Three times he instructs me to look and three times I

declare it to be empty. Because he is so insistent I fetch the jar to show him. To my surprise it is not empty.

I do not understand. It is not possible. I know the jar is empty. But I can see that it is not! I recall the stranger's promise on the morning before. I did not believe him. It is a great mystery. Perhaps he really is a holy man!

Six weeks pass. Every day we eat bread and I use all the flour and every drop of oil. I check to see that there is not the slightest bit remaining; and then each morning, when I look, there is enough flour and sufficient oil for just one more loaf. It is a miracle! The sea lavender withered long ago. The flour and oil remain. It alarms me a little to have a holy man in the house.

He is a strange, restless man, keeping very much to himself and not mixing with the townspeople. Every day he goes for long solitary walks, sometimes along the sea shore, sometimes in the mountains. Sometimes he is away from dawn to dusk, or he returns early, sits on the ground, leans against the cottage wall and stares, motionless, into the distance. He stays like this while the sun travels through the sky and the shadows lengthen. He seems to be in a trance. Other times I hear him talking to himself.

My neighbours tell me the market gossip, saying he is a refugee from Israel; a holy man who quarrelled with the King and put a curse on the land. Now he is fleeing from Queen Jezebel who wants to kill him. I do not like to hear this. Queen Jezebel is a powerful woman. She has spies everywhere. My neighbours tell me my guest is responsible for the drought! I cannot believe that! Not really! He is an unusual man, and it is true that I always find flour and oil, even when I know I have none, but why would such a man want to cause a drought, with all the suffering it creates? I do not believe it. It does not make sense. However, it is no good worrying about it. He is here now. I do not know how long he plans to stay and I do not like to ask him.

There is still no sign of rain. But there is no sign of our food running out, either. For that matter, there is no sign of my guest moving on. Perhaps it is all for the best. I have got used to having him around. I've got used to his peculiar ways.

Now my son is sick. He has been listless and off his food for several days but today he is much worse. He is feverish and he does not recognize me. He is seeing things that are not there. He imagines there are people watching him, I can see him looking at them, and he asks me to send them away. But there is no-one here. It frightens me. I have never seen him like this before. He cannot keep anything down, not even water. I wish I knew what to do. I give infusions of herbs, fennel and coriander, and I have even tried wormwood, all to no avail. I have dried burning pomegranate skin day and night in the house to ward off the evil spirits. I would go to the village shrine but my son is too sick. I dare not leave him. I would carry him there but he is too heavy for me.

The holy man is not here. He left at dawn to walk in the mountains. I fear that my son is sick because I have offended the God of the prophet who lodges with us. How have I sinned? What have I done to anger him? How should I make amends? I do not know.

My son is very weak now. He is hardly breathing. He is slipping away from me. I cannot bear it. Why do I have to suffer like this? I have tried to live a good life. I have sacrificed and kept all the feast days of all the gods. They are hard to please. It is not fair.

I sponge my child's hot brow. It is on fire. His eyes are glazed. His lips are cracked and his tongue is red and sore. I drip water into his mouth. I whisper to him, 'Do not die. Not now. Do not die. Please do not die. Do not leave me alone as your father has done. Stay with me, my child.'

My tears fall freely on to his face but he does not stir. His breathing is very rapid, very shallow, then stops. He is not breathing. I put my hand to his mouth to catch his breath. I put my ear close to his lips to listen. There is nothing. No breath. No sound. He looks as though he is asleep. Yes, of course. He is asleep. Not dead. My beautiful child, not dead.

I do not know how long I sit here, cradling my dead child in my arms. When it is dark the prophet comes. He comes to eat bread. There is no bread. Today I did not look for flour and oil. I was too busy with my son.

'Woman, where is the bread?' he asks.

I cannot answer. He comes into the cottage and sees me sitting with my son's lifeless body in my arms.

'What ails the boy?'

'He is dead!' I turn in anger and grief to the prophet, hardly knowing what I say, not caring, 'It is your fault! It is your fault! My son is dead. Why did you come here? Why didn't you leave us alone? I was ready for death. I had got it all worked out before you came here. You upset all my plans.' My words pour out. All my vague anxieties about the holy man, the gossip I have heard, the dead child growing cold in my arms. Why should I care any longer if I offend his God?

'I accepted my fate, then you came. You gave me hope. Now you have taken it away. Why did you come here and disturb our peace? We never asked you to come. Go away. Go away and leave me to grieve alone. My son is dead! Your God killed him. Why? Why did he do that? What have we ever done to him? Why did you come here?'

The holy man comes to me. He takes my child from my arms. He carries him away. To his room. He lays him upon his own bed, very gently. He throws himself on the body of my son and weeps. He cries aloud to his God, 'O Lord my God, this widow took pity on me. She fed me and gave me shelter. Have mercy upon her. Deliver her from evil. Restore her son to life I beseech you.' Very earnestly the prophet appeals to his God. If he had come sooner perhaps his God would have heard. If he had not been out walking all day in the mountains.

But it is too late. My son is dead. I cannot endure listening to his lamentation and entreaties. I walk away.

The holy man comes into the room. I hear him but I do not look at him.

'Mother?' I hear my son's voice, faint but distinct. It is an illusion. My grief is playing tricks on me.

'Mother?' I hear it again.

The holy man moves closer to me. I cannot look at him.

'Woman, here is your son,' he says. 'He is alive.'

'Mother, I'm hungry. Is there any bread?'

I turn. It is true. My son is alive, and hungry. I laugh and cry for joy. Alive! He is alive!

I take him from the prophet's arms, hold him close, hug him, kiss him. Impatiently he pushes me aside, 'Mother, I am hungry. Are you laughing or are you crying? What is the matter with you? Please give me some bread.'

I try to dry my eyes. I try to look at the prophet. I try to put my son down. Too much is happening all at once.

'Yes, yes. Of course you shall have bread, but first I must bake it. Go and fetch me the jar of oil. Are you well enough to fetch it?'

'Of course I am, Mother. Why not?' He runs off and I turn to the prophet. On my knees I say to him, 'Forgive me sir. Now I know you are indeed Elijah, the prophet of the Most High God. Now I know your words are true. I am sorry I doubted you. Thank you for giving me back my son.'

'Woman, you showed kindness to me in my hour of need. Should I not do the same for you? Now, shall I collect wood for the fire? We are all ready for some of your excellent bread, I think.'

# PRAYER

*Lord of Gethsemane who knew what it was to be alone and hungry in the desert, give me grace in times of despair to remember that you know my need better than I do. Help me to hold on in the darkest hour believing that the dawn will come. Enable me to know that no matter how afraid I feel, nor how hopeless things look, all will be well. Amen.*

## Suggested reading

1 Kings 17.1–24.

# 7

# THE PRIEST'S WIFE

*Elizabeth finally has a son*

⸙

For there is nothing God cannot do.
(Luke 1.37)

The harvest is over and the fields look strangely bare in the early morning mist. I hurry up the narrow mountain path to the spring, a bundle of clothes in my arms and immediately set about my task. I have not been there long before the sun rises, flooding the surrounding hills with its brilliant light. The cold water splashing my face makes me gasp. Brushing it away impatiently, I blink as the sunshine, reflected back from the surface of the stream, dazzles me. Then grasping the smooth stone more firmly in my swollen hands I grit my teeth and continue to pummel the washing. The pain must not prevent me from making the linen spotless. Intent on my task I am deaf to the approaching footsteps, the chattering voices.

'My, Elizabeth, you are up early. What is going on?'

'Yes, I am early. Zechariah has to go to the temple tomorrow and I must prepare his clothes.'

'Already? It is not so long ago that he was there.'

'I know, it does not seem long. But it is twice in every year. His second tour of duty always comes around just after the autumn harvest. It does seem to come quickly.

Time passes more quickly than ever at my age, I can tell you.'

'Come now, you are not so old,' they laugh. I laugh with them, but it is true, the seasons do seem to pass more quickly with advancing age. Zechariah and I are well advanced in years. Good years, they have been.

More women, weighed down by their laundry, join us beside the spring. The morning sun is dancing diamond-like on the rippling water. The birds sing and scratch about in the bushes. The women are like birds, I think, all clustering round the washing place.

'I hear Zechariah is off to the temple again,' one of them says, 'so we shall be losing you for a week. It is as well that there are no babies due in the village.'

'Yes, of course I shall go to Jerusalem, so that I can be close to Zechariah in the city,' I say.

I always go with my husband but I do not see him when we are there. He is closeted with the three hundred priests who are on duty for the seven days, in their own ritually clean quarters. To step outside the temple precincts would defile them. It is a most holy thing to lead the nation in worship. All other contact is forbidden until the end of the week when the priests return to their own homes and communities.

It is a cheerful scene at the river bank. Happy banter and merry laughter accompany the slapping and splashing of washing against the rocks. I enjoy this time. News from all around the region is exchanged.

'It is a good harvest this year.'

'Jacob's wife is expecting a new baby.'

'May Adonai bless her with another son!'

'James the potter has given a mohar to the son of Ezra for his daughter.'

'We shall have wedding celebrations!'

'How wonderful! It is too long since we had reason to rejoice.'

'We can rejoice in a good harvest.'

'That is true.'

I hear all the chatter but I do not join in. I do not need to do so. I have no news to share but I like to listen to theirs. These are my neighbours, my friends. We know one another intimately, especially since I am always called to attend the birth of each new baby. I have attended the mothers of many of the young women here at their birth. In fact, I have watched those babies grow to maturity, marry, and have then assisted when they have produced their own children. I learnt the skills of midwifery at my mother's knee, as they say, and a lifetime's experience has made me an expert. I am called to every sick bed. I am in attendance at every death. I have the gift of healing, of comforting others. I am not so good at comforting myself.

No-one sees my pangs of jealousy as I bring each new infant into the world. Not even Zechariah knows how I creep away to my secret place to weep bitterly. Only the Lord Adonai sees me. I endeavour to see that the face I present to the world is loving, kind and serene. The truth is, I am barren. I give new life to others. I have not been able to give a son to my husband. People believe I have accepted it. They think I no longer mind. I do mind.

'If I become bitter I shall only hurt myself,' I say in my heart. Sometimes angry, sometimes despairing, my secret prayers are frequently a running battle with God.

'Why? Why have you seen fit to leave me childless? It is not fair.'

I struggle continually to overcome the perpetual torment of envy and self-pity. But even as I pray I know that, like Job, I have no right to make demands of the Lord. The scripture tells us that Job said, 'The Lord gave, and now he has taken away. May his name be praised!'

The only difference between Job and me is that the Lord did not give me children so he cannot take them away. Resigned, I smile wryly to myself.

In our younger days Zechariah and I made endless sacrifices. With prayer and fasting we pleaded with the Lord for

68

a son, or even a daughter. But he was deaf. He did not hear us. I could not understand how the Lord Adonai could deny our request. What reason could he have? We discussed it often.

'We will make good parents,' we would tell each other.

'We can give a child a good home, a priest's home. A better home than many of our poor neighbours who are blessed with too many mouths to feed. It is so unfair.'

It must be that God cannot hear us. Should we call louder? Surely not! The Lord our God is not deaf like pagan gods.

'Have we sinned?' I would ask myself. 'Have we offended Adonai in some way? But if so, how? Is it possible to sin greatly without knowing? Does the Lord ruthlessly punish the sin of ignorance?'

Many such questions trouble me to this day. I am as sure as I can be that both Zechariah and I live blamelessly, keeping the law in every detail. More than that, we rejoice to do so. It is not an arduous duty. Are we then guilty of the greatest sin of all, that of pride? . . . The uncertainty, that is what makes it so hard to bear.

In those early days Zechariah wept with me. The law entitled him to divorce me and take another wife, but he loved me so much he would not do it. His love for me was greater than his desire to have a son. He knew, and I knew too, any woman would have been glad to have him because he was handsome, industrious, and he owned a plot of fertile land. So, because we could not have children Zechariah threw himself into his work and encouraged me to do the same.

'The Lord has seen fit to withhold his blessing,' was all Zechariah said, 'He knows what he is about. It is not for us to question him. We must keep faith and do our duty. He will reward us in his own time and in his own way. And if not, we will still keep faith. In the end, all will be explained.'

The years have passed happily enough. Zechariah, absorbed in his work, does not mention our sadness. I take my lead from him, devoting myself to my needlework, to supporting him in his priestly office, and to serving our neighbours. I belong to the group of women who work month in and month out to weave new curtains for the temple. There are twenty-six curtains in all, they are huge and intricately woven. It is a full-time job to replace two each year. I also embroider my husband's priestly garments. I hardly notice the dull ache, the emptiness, at the centre of my being but it is there all the time.

Today we rise early to go to Jerusalem. I pick some herbs, fennel and parsley to take with me to sell in the market place. We leave the shady terraces of our village where the vines grow in profusion and walk along the track which meanders up and down through the hills to the city. I am excited. Our village is not far from the city of David but I have no reason to visit it unless Zechariah is on duty in the temple. It is a great adventure for me. I have bathed in the river and oiled my greying hair. Zechariah will bathe in the temple pools reserved for priests.

We enter the city by the Sheep Gate and Zechariah embraces me before going on his way directly to the temple. I make for the lodgings I use whenever I visit Jerusalem. I am anxious to deposit my belongings and then to amble through the market before finding a shady place to sit and sell my bundles of herbs.

In the evening I come with other women to the temple court especially set aside for us and climb the steps to the screened gallery. From here I may be able to catch sight of Zechariah performing his sacred duties. A choir of Levites begins to sing, new wood is added to the fires and the sweet smell of incense wafts across the air to where we are standing. Then I hear the noise of pipes, drums and cymbals and I know the lamb has been slain. I can see many of the priests moving slowly and gracefully about the inner court but I cannot see Zechariah. The smell of the burnt offering mingles with the incense and three priests move up the steps towards the Holy Place. One looks like Zechariah but I cannot be sure. It seems unlikely. In all his years of service he has never been the one to enter the inner sanctum of the most Holy Place. I know the commission is assigned by lot but Zechariah has never had the good fortune to be chosen. How wonderful if it is really him I can see.

I wish I had a better view. My eyes are not as good as they used to be. While I am straining to get a better look the three priests disappear behind the veil of the temple. They are in the Holy Place, in the presence of the Lord, the God of Abraham and Isaac. A thin wisp of smoke appears above the sacred canopy and drifts lazily over the waiting company. Soon the sickly sweet smell of the hallowed incense fills the air, overflowing into the temple courtyard. The whole congregation joins the choirs singing praise to God.

The cycle of the music comes to an end and there is an uncomfortable shuffling in the crowd. A restlessness. I see the priests in the temple courtyard moving less gracefully. They move about, now in little clusters, now moving apart. Something seems to be wrong. Gradually every eye is turned in complete silence towards the Holy Place. The priest does not appear to give the farewell blessing. Two priests raise silver trumpets and sound a long note. The priest still does not appear.

What is wrong? I have a strange premonition. Not fear. Apprehension and, yes, anticipation. But why?

Minutes pass. The people cannot leave until the priest emerges to dismiss us. We wait. And we wait. At first patiently, expectantly, but when the priest fails to appear the crowd becomes restive. I wonder, 'Is he ill?'

Then, like wind blowing through a field of wheat, the congregation begins to kneel. Over the bowed heads I see my husband. He has changed. He stands unsteadily. He looks ahead, eyes shining, fixed on some distant point above the temple. Other priests hurry to his side and support him. A murmur runs through the gathering, 'The priest has had a vision. He has spoken with the Most High. Praise the Lord. Praise be to the Holy One.'

Eventually, with the assistance of his colleagues and with silent gestures, Zechariah blesses and dismisses the congregation. My husband has been struck dumb.

In the dark winter months I grow fat. Torrential rains wash the land. It is cold. Eventually spring returns. Suddenly the midday sun is hot in the sky but the nights are still cold. The fields are ready for planting. Zechariah will not be going to serve his tour of duty in the temple. He is still dumb.

We meet again at the washing place, my neighbours and I, to launder our clothes. The cheerful banter and exchange of gossip continues as always. I notice my neighbours looking at me curiously. One of them says, 'Elizabeth, if I did not know better I would think you were expecting a child. You have grown fat over the winter months and you have an extraordinary radiance about you. You look ten years younger.'

I grin at her. 'I am pregnant.'

The babbling voices cease abruptly. All the bustling activity stops. Upturned heads gaze at me.

'That is impossible.'

'Impossible or not, I am expecting a child!'

The women gather round me all laughing and talking at once.

'Are you sure?'

'How has it happened?'

'When? When is it due?'

'How do you feel?'

'Come here and sit down.'

'Let me take your washing.'

'How will you manage with a young child under your feet?'

'We will help you. Everyone will help you.'

It is wonderful. I have never had so much attention. There has never been such interest and such laughter in our village. My baby is famous and he is not yet born. I know I shall have a son because that is what Zechariah wrote on a tablet, when he came from the temple.

It is all very strange and very wonderful. Zechariah explained to me, with words written on his slate and with gestures, that in the Holy Place an angel spoke to him. The angel said I would have a son. Naturally my husband found this hard to believe. The angel said Zechariah, because of his unbelief, would not be able to speak until the child was born. It would be a sign.

I do not need a sign. The evidence is in my body. But it is hard to believe! I am making a journey. An inner journey. After all these years of assisting other young women to give birth I thought that nothing could surprise me. But, strange as it may seem, I find the experience awesome. I feel as if I am the first woman in the world ever to have a baby. It feels so special, so privileged, so unreal.

With my husband I am making a new human being, quite unlike any other. What will he be like? What will he do? The angel, Zechariah says, proclaimed that our son will be strong and mighty, like the prophet Elijah. He will prepare the way of the Lord.

These are wonderful words. What can they mean? I pat my fat belly and sing to my unborn son, 'Let us praise the Lord, the God of Israel!' In reply the child in my womb kicks my hand, and I laugh.


### PRAYER

*Lord, lover of the humble heart, I thank you for the example of Elizabeth who learnt to accept with serenity the circumstances of her life. Let me, like her, check all bitterness.*

*Like her may I learn to accept those things I cannot*

*change. May I also learn to rise to unexpected blessings and responsibilities, even if I feel myself too old or too inadequate for them.*

*Give me grace always to trust you for those gifts which you withhold, as well as for those gifts you entrust to my keeping. Amen.*

### Suggested reading

Luke 1.5–25; 57–66.

**8**

# DO NOT TROUBLE ME

## A *desperate mother refuses to take 'no' for an answer*

───────

Then a man came and wrestled with him until just before
daybreak. . . . The man said, 'Let me go; daylight is coming.' 'I
won't, unless you bless me,' Jacob answered.

(Genesis 32.24–26)

Two women in their early thirties sit grinding corn in the
courtyard of a stone cottage. Shaded by a dried palm
canopy, they work in comfortable harmony. They have
been close friends since childhood. One of them looks
thoughtfully at the other before speaking.

'Bilhah?'

'Yes?'

'I have decided to go and see the prophet, the healer.'

Shocked, her companion stops the grinding stone. She
has heard, of course, the gossip about the prophet who
is travelling through the region. She has heard how he
has powers to heal the sick. But while news of him has
reached her village the area he is visiting is several days
journey away. The terrain is mountainous. Few caravans
travel that way and it is not an expedition to be undertaken
lightly. Besides which, even if her friend Dinah could
make the trip, the prophet would surely have nothing to

do with her. Bilhah looks at the way her friend's head is thrown back slightly, her lips clamped tightly together. It is an all too familiar look of defiance. It means she has made a decision and will not easily be moved. Even so, Bilhah has to try and she says firmly, 'Even if the journey were possible, you know you cannot do that!'

'Why not?'

'He is a Jew, a rabbi.'

'So?'

'You are a foreigner. Jews have nothing to do with strangers. We are offensive to them.'

'I have heard that this man is different. He speaks to anyone, even Romans, as though they were equal to him.'

'Maybe, but not to a woman.'

'Yes, he does. I have heard he does. He is not like other rabbis. He even has women amongst his followers.'

'Only rich and influential women. Women married to important officials.'

'How do you know?'

'I know he will not have anything to do with you.'

'He will! I believe he will. If he is a holy man, as they say, he will not turn me away.'

'Oh, Dinah! You are making a terrible mistake.'

'Well, I have got to do something. I cannot just sit around and watch my child suffering as she does. Her condition is getting worse all the time. First of all the physicians said that she had a fever and that it would pass.'

'She did have a fever.'

'That was months ago. Now she cannot sit still for an instant and I am told she has an excitable nature.'

'Well, she has. Maybe you expect too much of her, Dinah. You should just give her simple tasks to do.'

'Bilhah, her movements are so erratic now that she cannot even stir the cooking pot safely. You see her. You know what she is like. She is getting worse all the time.'

Bilhah does not answer. She bites her lip. It is true. The

little girl, Deborah, is very odd. She was once so full of life but since having the fever her movements and behaviour have become bizarre. It is tragic. She is such a pretty child but now the other children in the village point their finger and laugh at her.

'You know what they say at the village well. They say my beautiful child has a demon. You do not believe it, do you, Bilhah?'

'No. Of course not.' The answer is a little too quick. A little too emphatic.

'I keep incense burning at my household shrine day and night, Bilhah. Every day I offer fresh bread and wine to the gods. Why do they not heed me?'

'I do not know, Dinah. These things are very hard to understand. But it is the way of life. You must accept your fate and be at peace.'

'I will not accept it while there is something I can do. If our gods do not hear me maybe this man of god, this Israelite, may hear me. If I do not ask I shall never know. Surely you understand?'

'Deborah needs you here. A sick child needs her mother. You cannot go off and leave her.'

'Who else will plead for her? My mother understands. She will care for Deborah while I am away. I must go myself to see this man. I will throw myself on his mercy. Beg for his help. It may be the only opportunity I shall have, now while he is visiting our coasts . . . You will help me, Bilhah?'

Bilhah looks doubtfully at her friend as they continue to turn the heavy grinding stone. It is true that the stories about the healer have been unusual, even for an itinerant prophet, but even if he were willing to listen to Dinah, what good could he do? He could not use his power to heal Deborah from such a distance, and surely not even this man of surprises would go out of his way to visit a Syrophonecian village. It is hopeless and she says, 'The braying of an ass cannot reach heaven, Dinah!'

'True, but with persistence a mouse can pierce wood, Bilhah!'

Their eyes meet over the grinding stone and, forgetting their disagreement for a moment, they laugh.

'I see you mean to do this thing. Of course I will help you in any way I can.'

Dinah smiles her gratitude. 'Now, I have things to do. Let us finish here quickly. I must leave at dawn.'

'Oh, Dinah, dear friend, it may be foolish but you have courage. I hope I would do the same thing in your position. I wish you well.'

'Thank you.' Dinah takes a deep breath and bends her head over the grinding stone. They work in silence for a while before she blurts out, 'I know you are right. I am afraid the holy man will refuse to see me. It is foolhardy. Why should he bother with me? There are many Jewish children who are sick and in need. But,' she pauses, and continues thoughtfully, 'we are all children of Abraham and, if he is truly a man of god, do not you think, when he sees me, he might make an exception? I am appealing to him for my child. How can he turn me away?'

'I hope the gods will reward your faith.'

'They will. They will.'

'The shrine of Arsiya is not far from the village. I will go to lay a witness stone and make an offering of the best grain and grapes for your success. She is a woman and looks after womankind. She will bless your journey.'

'Thank you, Bilhah.' Dinah answers, vaguely wondering if a sacrifice to Arsiya would please the god of Israel. She has heard he is a jealous god.

At dawn Dinah is ready. She rolls her best clean tunic into her blanket and slings it over her shoulder, together with a leather water container. In her hand she carries a little rush basket containing all the provisions she thinks she will need. A few barley loaves, some dried fish and a little goat's cheese wrapped in vine leaves. Bilhah rises early to see her on her way. The two friends part sadly.

Dinah has not walked many miles before she begins to have doubts. As she treads along the dusty road her confidence wanes. Her brave words to Bilhah evaporate. Her resolve falters. This, now, is reality. She is alone. The journey is dangerous. She is far from the security of her village. She has never been so far from home. Her feet are caked with dirt, her hair unkempt, her soiled clothes cling uncomfortably to her hot body. The smell of travelling lingers in her nostrils while sweat and tears pour down her face. Arms and legs heavy with exhaustion, she longs for the familiar faces she has left behind. She is afraid.

Hot days and cold nights increase her anxiety; she dreams of wild animals and impassable crevices. Her fear nearly makes her turn back. Only the thought of Deborah's agonized face and painful convulsive movements, keeps her going. She wonders if her mother is coping, if her daughter is missing her, if she should have remained at home as Bilhah said. Full of doubts she asks herself, 'Will the healer, Son of David, agree to see me? Will he help me? Will he still be in the region when I arrive?'

Desperation speeds her on, lends her courage. Despair gives birth to hope. Refusing to give way to her doubts she comforts herself with the words of one of the many proverbs of her people. A people who have learnt to expect the unexpected in life. Over and over as she takes each weary step she whispers, 'It has even snowed on trees red with cherries. It has even snowed on trees red with cherries.' Impossible things do happen, she assures herself.

The hours pass. She stumbles on. Heart thumping in her chest she pleads to the unknown god, 'May it please you, Lord of heaven and earth, Keeper of day and night, to hear my cry. May the offerings of my friend Bilhah be acceptable at the high place of Arsiya. Hear my cry O Mighty One.' Dinah struggles to find the right words. 'Deliver my daughter from the evil eye. Let her be as she once was, like other children. Let her be whole. Comfort her while I am away and give strength to my mother to care for her. O Holy One, may the healer, the Son of David, see me and have compassion on me. Spare my daughter, I beseech you.'

Her prayers are like lotion to her feet. She no longer notices the blisters which burn and the stones which cut. Oblivious to the curious glances of other travellers, her mission consumes her. She must see the healer. He must help her.

Eventually, exhausted, she arrives at the town where he is staying. Ignoring her hunger, and without pausing to wash and change into the clean tunic which she packed so carefully, she sets out to find him. It is easier than she expects. She simply follows the crowd to a grassy slope not far from the village well. There he is, a curiously striking figure, seated on a rock in the shade of a pomegranate tree. Dinah is surprised. He looks like any other man. He has no outstanding features. What is it that attracts the people? Also, the healer is much younger than she expects. How could the fame of one so young travel so far?

A group of men sit on the lower slopes, listening intently to every word the young man speaks. Dinah, coming closer, sees that women and children are also there in the crowd. This is an extraordinary sight. It would never happen in her village for men to sit with women and children. When she is close enough to see more clearly she is astonished, 'Why, he is surrounded by children, sitting on his knee, playing with his sandals, tugging at his beard but he does not seem to mind at all.' Her wonder at what she sees renews her courage.

'So, if he cares for children he will not, he cannot, refuse to help me when he hears about my child.'

Dinah draws nearer. The healer is telling a story. He speaks with authority. His melodious voice recounts a tale of a shepherd who has lost a sheep. On and on the narrative flows in tones, now soothing, now strong, hypnotizing his audience. Dinah moves into an imaginary world where her own troubles are forgotten. She is the shepherd, anxious for the lost sheep, feeling the brambles tear at her skin, feeling the dryness of her mouth, experiencing the shepherd's joy when the sheep is found. She is enthralled.

All the time he speaks the story-teller's eyes move to and fro across the crowd, as if searching for someone. Dinah, standing some distance away, nevertheless feels him looking at her. For a moment their eyes meet.

Suddenly she feels exposed; feels he knows her inmost secrets. Her cheeks burn and, unnerved, she hastily lowers her head. When she next dares to look his gaze has moved on but her heart pounds painfully in her chest; her breath comes rapidly; she gasps for air. The hammering in her ears makes her fear she may faint. Glancing to right and left she wonders if anyone has noticed. But no, every eye is fixed on the story-teller.

The sun is sinking in the sky and the distant hills are turning rose grey when the man stops speaking. Reluctantly the people rise and slowly begin to disperse. Most follow the footpath to the town but some move off in other directions. Dinah, sitting on the fringe of the crowd, is apprehensive now. Enchanted by the stories, overwhelmed by the throng, she feels insignificant and vulnerable. A cool breeze blows. There is movement on every side. This is her moment to act. She has reached her destination but she hesitates. After so many days her courage finally fails.

'I am too tired. I am hungry. What am I thinking of? How can I, a stranger and a woman, dare to approach this holy man? I thought I might approach him quietly, in private. I did not know there would be so many people. What can I say to him?'

While she hesitates the teacher and his closest friends leave. In despair she puts her head in her hands, and notices for the first time her bedraggled appearance. She doesn't belong here. She has no right to approach the healer. The situation is hopeless. No-one takes any notice as Dinah gets to her feet and stumbles away. Finding a deserted spot she slumps to the ground, prostrates herself, and sobs uncontrollably. Memories of Deborah's face, ugly and distressed, her pitiful contortions, come to mind. Inwardly she sees her child's uncomprehending grief. Deborah is like an animal caught in a trap.

'Oh God, help me,' she prays.

When the outburst subsides she sits staring into space until she shivers in the evening breeze. Cold and hunger arouse her.

'I must eat,' she tells herself, briskly 'and I must find shelter for the night.'

The need for action restores Dinah's vitality. Rising swiftly to her feet she turns towards the town. As she makes her way past the outlying cottages an elderly woman, the wife of a poor fisherman approaches, regarding her with obvious curiosity. Dinah addresses her, using a term of respect, 'Mother, I have come from a distant village to see the healer. I need lodgings for the night. Water to wash and hot soup to warm me. I have money . . .'

Before she can finish the old woman smiles, 'You are welcome to stay with us, daughter. Our home is humble but warm and dry. Help me with the water pot and then honour us as our guest. When we have eaten we will talk of the teacher; of the wonderful stories he tells; and of the marvellous things he does.'

The old couple, delighted to have a visitor, concerned that she looks so weary, feed her well on mutton broth. Dinah, feeling revived, is anxious to hear all they can tell her of the man she has come to find, and they talk long into the night. The miracle worker is called Jesus, they tell her, a carpenter's son from Nazareth. They listen to Dinah with interested concern, marvelling at her conviction that the story-teller whom she had never seen could heal her daughter, astonished at her persistence. Not until the oil burns low in the lamps do they allow their guest to retire. Thankful to have found such friends, Dinah sleeps soundly in a corner of the cottage, on a rug laid on fresh straw.

At break of day they rise and feast on olives, goat's cheese and unleavened bread, warmed on the embers of the previous night's fire. The old couple give Dinah warm milk, fresh from the goat, to drink. They assure her that she has nothing to fear in approaching Jesus of Nazareth. He is a good man who will not turn her away.

Cheered by their encouragement Dinah once more follows the crowd to a place where the teacher is sitting, his voice ringing out calm but strong over the hillside. Her confidence renewed Dinah says to herself, 'I must get closer. I must be near enough to speak to him as soon as I get an opportunity.'

She begins to edge her way through the crowd, ignoring the occasional hiss and hostile glance of those who identify her as a foreigner. Some draw away, protecting themselves with their cloaks, treating her as an untouchable. She no longer minds, but continues to push her way forward. The crowd is moving all the time, quite rapidly.

'What is happening?' she asks. No-one replies and she hears others on either side, to the front and behind, ask the same question.

'What is happening?'

The answer moves like water through the mass of people, a low murmuring like a wave breaking on the shore, eventually taking the form of words,

'He is leaving! The teacher is leaving us!'

'No! No!'

'Ask him to stay a little longer.'

'We need him! We need him here.'

'He must not leave us!'

'Ask him to stay.'

Dinah is horrified. Leaving? Now? Before she has spoken to him?

'No! No!' She hears herself crying out. 'No! No! Do not go. Healer! Teacher!'

Still the crowd carries her along, moving relentlessly towards the road out of the town. How can she attract his attention?

'Son of David,' she cries out, 'Son of David! Have mercy on me, sir!'

People jostle her on every side, shushing her, pushing her aside.

'Quiet woman! Why should he listen to you? He is leaving.'

'Son of David!' Dinah shouts all the louder, and clutches at the clothes of the men who follow Jesus.

Jesus is now very close to Dinah but he shows no sign of hearing her cries.

'Son of David! Healer! Teacher! Have mercy on me, sir! My daughter has a demon and is in a terrible condition.'

He ignores her. She cannot believe it. She continues to follow him, calling out, ignoring the hostility of the crowd.

Finally Jesus stops. His disciples complain, 'This woman is a stranger. She is following us and making a spectacle of herself. She is embarrassing us. Send her away!'

Jesus turns and looks at Dinah. He shows no sign of recognition but she senses he knows her as the dishevelled woman who met his eyes the previous day. Now she does not blush. She is confident he will hear her. Unsmilingly he says, 'What do you want?'

'Sir, my daughter is very sick. You can heal her. I know you can. You only have to say the word and she will be well. I know she will.'

Jesus says sternly, 'I have been sent only to the lost sheep of the people of Israel.'

His words are like a shock of cold water. Her mind races. This is not the answer she expects. It is not the right answer. She cannot have heard him. What is happening? He is wrong! She *knows* he is wrong! Dinah looks at Jesus. Blood drains from her face, her lips part and her eyes dilate. She thinks she will faint. Everything becomes blurred. Has she come so far and endured so much only to be turned away? Has she been mistaken? Will he really refuse her just because she belongs to the wrong race?

Dinah throws herself down on her knees and clasps her hands tight in supplication, 'Help me, sir!' she begs.

Jesus replies, 'It isn't right to take the children's food and throw it to the dogs.'

Kneeling at his feet, her hands clasped together like a vice, Dinah's dark eyes are riveted to his. Her whole body screams in silent supplication. For a long time she remains thus. Finally, desperately, she whispers, 'Even the dogs eat the crumbs that fall from their master's table.'

A gasp of shocked surprise rustles through the crowd. A momentary pause. Then, while the crowd holds its breath, Jesus suddenly laughs. 'You are a woman of great faith!' he says, 'what you want will be done for you.'

Dinah all but throws herself into his arms. Laughing and crying she says, 'Thank you, sir. Thank you, sir.'

She makes no effort to check the tears flowing down her cheeks. Crying, smiling and laughing by turns; clapping her hands together and dancing she turns to hug the women standing nearby. They no longer shun her. They are delighted. As Jesus leaves the town, they welcome Dinah to their homes, insisting that she should rest, and eat, before setting off on her homeward journey.

Dinah returns to her village on a donkey laden with gifts from the townspeople, who are anxious to make amends for their initial hostility. Slow as the creature is, the miles speed by under his clip-clopping hooves. As she approaches her village she sees Bilhah and Deborah silhouetted against the hazy midday sky. They run hand in hand towards her.

'Mother, mother! See! I am well again. I can walk and run. And I can stir the cooking pot and fetch water from the well. Look at me, Mother!'

'Yes, Deborah. I see you.'

Dinah meets her friend's eyes. 'Did you know, Bilhah, how important it is to allow the dogs to eat the crumbs under the table?'

## PRAYER

*Lord Jesus, I thank you for the example of the woman who was an outsider but who dared to come to you; taking you at your word and challenging your love.*

*Give me grace to claim your blessing in every circumstance of life, that I may honour and praise your name. Amen.*

### *Suggested reading*

Matthew 15.21–28.

# 9

# AN AMBITIOUS MOTHER

*A fisherman's wife wants the best
for her sons*

---

If one of you wants to be great he must be the servant of the
rest, and if one of you wants to be first, he must be your slave.

(Matthew 20.26–27)

The chill morning breeze drifts over the village from the
inland sea. Zara sits outside the cottage door effortlessly
throwing the shuttle back and forth across the loom. She
shivers, pausing to secure a linen square over her silver
grey hair, indifferent to the restless child who is watching
her. Anna dare not speak. Something is wrong. Grandmother is frowning, her normally happy face is dark
with anger. Eventually, bored with the uneasy silence, Anna
wanders behind the loom to study the woven canvas
from the back. Deep in thought she returns to her grandmother's side. Anna has noticed a subtle difference in the
way the rug develops on each side of the loom. Forgetting
the need for caution she blurts out, 'Grandmother, why
does the pattern look so untidy from this side?'

Zara continues to weave.

'Grandmother, have you made a mistake? Look! It
looks all wrong on this side. Come and see!'

Eventually noticing Anna's persistent voice, but without

looking up or pausing in her rhythmic movements, Zara answers, a little testily, 'The pattern grows from where I sit. You are looking at the underside. No-one will see it when the rug is finished and lying on the floor.'

'That is a shame,' Anna answers, undeterred. 'I wish both sides could be as beautiful as each other.'

'Then the pattern would be meaningless.'

'Why?'

'Because it is impossible to develop the design on this side, where it is important and still keep a sense of order on the other side.'

At this moment Anna's mother calls, 'The stones are nearly hot enough for baking. Come and help us to make the bread.'

'I am helping Grandmother,' Anna protests.

'You are being a nuisance. We need you here.'

Reluctantly Anna moves across the dusty courtyard to help her mother and aunt knead the dough to put into the hot earth oven.

Left to herself Zara continues to weave. Her thoughts, angry and confused, on the events of the past few weeks, on the furious argument she had with Zebedee, her husband, the previous evening.

Meanwhile, Zebedee, hard at work with his hired hands is engaged with his own thoughts. It has been a long night. The elusive fish escape the fishing fleet until dawn, but Zebedee, persisting when his neighbours lose heart, has full nets to land. Now, with his men, he sorts and cleans the catch, ready for market. Finally they kindle a fire and squat around it. Selecting the fish too small to sell, they cook and eat a hearty meal. They sit, sometimes silent, sometimes in desultory chatter, lingering over the meal as the sun rises higher in the sky. Zebedee is in no hurry to climb the stony path to his cottage. He fears a repeat performance, another scene with his volatile wife.

Though accustomed to her passionate nature he has

rarely seen her so angry as she was the previous evening. The moment comes when Zebedee has no excuse to delay any longer and, feeling better for a full stomach, he joins his companions and they make their way back to their small but prosperous community. The peaceful scene at the cottage as he approaches reassures him; Zara working steadily at the loom, his daughters-in-law busy baking, the absence of raised voices; these are good signs. The silent tongues and his granddaughter Anna's subdued demeanour; these, however, signal prudence. He must tread warily; suddenly he feels exhausted.

Zara hearing him approach, looks up. He barely has time to greet her before she speaks, 'I have come to a decision. I know what I am going to do,' her voice is firm. Then, more hesitantly, 'But I should like to know what you think, Zebedee.'

'Woman,' he says wearily. 'I have been out all night. Surely it can wait?'

'No, Zebedee. I have made my mind up and I must act before I think better of it.' She pauses, ever so briefly to ask, 'Have you eaten?'

'Yes. We had a good catch and we grilled fish on the beach. Well now,' he says, settling himself down beside her, 'what is this great decision that you have made?'

'I am going to go to speak to Jesus, son of Joseph, myself. You must persuade James and John to come with me.'

'Oh, and what are you going to say?'

'I shall mention that our sons have made great sacrifices to follow him around the country these past three years. So have we, if it comes to that. I shall remind him that they left you to cope with the business alone, without a second thought. I shall point out that they've been with him from the beginning. He could not have wished for more loyal or more devoted disciples. And ...'

She hesitates.

'And ... ?'

'Well, I shall . . . suggest,' she chooses her words carefully, 'that he is indebted to them.' She hesitates and scowls again. Zebedee remains silent. She mutters, almost to herself, 'I would not have minded, you know. I would not have minded. But James and John were working alongside Simon and Andrew right from the first. They all joined him the same day, within minutes of each other. But that Simon! He is always pushing himself forward; always the first to speak; he is impetuous. You never know what he is going to do next; never know where you are with him. Why should he be favoured above my sons? That is what I should like to know. What special gifts has he got? My two may not be so quick to speak up but they are cleverer than Simon. They weigh things up; think things over. They are dependable. I should rather be with them when a storm blows up at sea than with Simon. And to think . . .' Zara's voice rises. She goes red in the face, grits her jaw and clenches her fists. Zebedee waits for the explosion. 'To think that the teacher has named Simon, Peter. A Rock! Him! What is there that is rock-like about him? He is so volatile! More like a volcano. What is there about him that is solid and dependable? That is what I should like to know! Why has Jesus chosen him?' She pauses for breath. 'Well, if he is to have a special place in the promised kingdom, our sons deserve it too!' Zara picks up the shuttle and starts to throw it vigorously across the loom.

Like a squall on Lake Galilee, her rage passes. But not her intention. Not many days later she is packing a few belongings in her shawl to travel with others of her neighbours to Jerusalem. They are going to celebrate the Passover Feast. Jesus will lead the pilgrimage, with James and John and the other disciples. Zara decides this will be a good opportunity to get alongside the teacher and make her petition. She also reasons it may be beneficial to take Anna along with her because the child's pretty looks and captivating manner melt many hearts.

Whenever the travellers take time to rest on their journey

Jesus spends time telling them wonderful stories and Zara is captivated. It is the first time she has really listened to him. His voice is mellow and warm, and, although he is only the son of the carpenter at Nazareth, he speaks with surprising authority. Whenever he looks at her it is as if there is no-one else present at all; just Zara and Jesus. He seems to know her through and through. She finds it confusing; comforting but also rather frightening.

One day, Zara sees Jesus watching the children gleefully collecting flowers to make garlands to hang round their necks. The disciples are having a fierce debate but the teacher does not appear to notice. Anna approaches Jesus shyly and offers him the garland in her hand. He smiles and bends his head so that she can reach up to hang the flowers round his neck. Then he calls to his disciples, 'Come here, to me.' The disciples are instantly alert. They hurry to his side, ready to send away the children, who are disturbing him.

'No,' Jesus says, 'You don't understand. Look at these children. Study them. Unless you become like them, you cannot enter the kingdom of God. Whoever would be greatest in my kingdom must become like a little child.'

It is true that they do not understand but they sit down and listen as he begins to teach them many things. Zara no longer hears his words, encouraged that Jesus has noticed Anna, she moves to position herself between James and John. As soon as Jesus finishes speaking she grasps her sons by the elbows, 'Now. Speak to him now.'

They shake her off.

'Listen to me,' Zara pleads, 'you have been with the teacher from the very first day, just like Simon and Andrew. Simon has been promised the keys of the Kingdom. You also should be honoured. Ask him. All you have to do is to ask him. Please. What harm can it do to ask?'

'Perhaps you are right. But, not now. Not yet. It is not appropriate to ask for favours when he has just finished preaching, Mother.'

'This evening, then. After the evening meal. You will speak to him then? I'll go with you.'

They hesitate. Zara persists until, reluctantly, they agree to her request.

In the quiet of the evening, when Jesus is sitting apart from the disciples, Zara takes Anna by the hand and goes to him, with James and John.

'Sir,' Zara says quietly. 'We have something to ask you.'

'What is it?'

'See, this is my little granddaughter, Anna. She is the child of my son here, your disciple, John. His brother, James, is her uncle. These are my sons. They are the sons of Zebedee, my husband, the fisherman. You remember? You saw them together one day, mending their nets, as you passed by and you called them to go with you.'

Jesus listens. He does not answer.

'I know you are a great teacher, and that one day you will establish a new order. You have honoured Simon by setting him apart as a leader. Please sir, will you promise me, the mother of these two fine young men, my sons, my only sons, that they will sit, one on your right and the other on your left, in your kingdom?'

Zara holds her breath, clutching Anna's hand. For a long time Jesus does not speak. Zara wonders if he has heard her. Eventually when he speaks his voice sounds far away, 'You do not know what you ask.'

Then he looks at her sons and inquires, 'Can you drink the cup that I am to drink?'

'We can,' they answer firmly.

Jesus sighs and says, 'You shall indeed drink my cup,' and he pauses, deep in thought. 'But to sit on my right or on my left is not for me to grant; that honour is for those to whom it has already been assigned by my Father.' So saying, he rises and walks away towards the mountain. Zara looks after him, puzzled by the apparent sadness in his manner. There is something here she doesn't understand. But then, there are many things about this strange teacher that she doesn't understand. She doesn't even really grasp the full meaning of his wonderful stories. Mystified she turns to ask her sons what they think of it, but they have slipped away. She finds she and Anna are standing alone, still holding hands.

The next day Zara hears Jesus telling his disciples that if they wish to be truly great leaders they will have to become, not like servants, but like slaves, to one another. This, she feels, is too extreme. It is just about the most foolish thing she has ever heard but, somehow, when Jesus says it she almost thinks it makes sense.

Throughout the rest of the pilgrimage Zara is quiet and thoughtful. She finds herself listening more closely to the stories of Jesus and the wisdom of his words. She feels that her life is being turned upside down. There is so much that doesn't make sense to her, but she finds herself longing to accept his teachings.

Several weeks later as dawn breaks over the Galilean hills, Zebedee climbs the stony path to his cottage once more, puzzling over the change in his wife. Since her trip to Jerusalem she is calmer, more thoughtful and considerate. Not that she was anything but a dutiful wife before, but now the restless, agitated spirit has gone.

He hears the happy banter before the cottage comes into sight and there is Zara sitting at her loom with Anna by her side. She throws the shuttle back and forth, as before, effortlessly. Her skilful fingers and practised eye are intent on her craft. The angry frown has gone, although she is deep in thought.

'See, Anna,' she says 'here where I work the story unfolds. On the other side, where you say the threads appear dark and tangled, the pattern is also growing. The untidiness, as you call it, behind the loom holds together the lovely colours which everyone will enjoy when the rug is finished. This is what life is like. When sadness and troubles disturb us we are afraid and angry. But the God of Abraham sees the whole canvas of our lives. What is dark to us may be very beautiful to him. We do not understand now, but one day we shall. Like the seasons of the year our lives have a rhythm which may not always be pleasant but which is necessary. All that is required of us is that we should be faithful in whatever duties we have to perform.'

'I do not understand, Grandmother.'

'No, Anna, nor do I. Not exactly. But I look at my rug, and I am comforted to know that one day it will be complete.'

'But, will you not make another rug when you have finished this one, Grandmother?'

Zara catches Zebedee's eye and laughs. 'I am sure I shall. Now go and help your mother while Grandpa and I talk.'

## PRAYER

*Son of God, there is so much that I do not understand. Like any mother I have high hopes for my children. I want the very best for them. I want them to have opportunities which I never had. It is right and good that I should feel like this, but grant me the humility to understand that I do not always, necessarily, know what is in their best interests.*

*Help me also to remember that my children are a gift. Give me patience to allow them to grow and make mistakes. Grant me wisdom and integrity when they ask difficult questions, and faith when I am at a loss to understand them.*

*Help me to know that my hopes and aspirations are finite whereas your truth is infinite. Give me grace also to recognize that everybody is somebody's child and may I have a generous heart towards every person I meet. Amen.*

*Suggested reading*

Matthew 20.20–28.

# 10

# WHO HAS SINNED?

*The mother of a traitor wonders
where she failed*

———◦———

And now I give you a new commandment: love one another.
As I have loved you, so you must love one another.

(John 13.34)

It is the Sabbath, and I sit here alone, in this garden, with
my grief. I do not know how long I have been sitting here.
It is evening; and I am cold.

I have no name. No-one has given me a name. No-one
thinks to mention me. I have no importance . . . It is as
though I do not exist. It would be better if I hadn't been
born. Then, perhaps, things would be different now.

But I do exist. I am a village woman from the hill country.
There is nothing exceptional about my life. My home and
family are no different from any other. My husband is a
good man. While many of my babies died in infancy, as is
the way of life, yet still we are blessed with a large family.
Children and grandchildren. I thank God for it. As I sit
here I relive the past months . . .

I always do my best, but somewhere I have gone wrong.
Where have I gone wrong? It is not knowing. That is the
hard thing. Our family life seems content, in harmony with

the seasons; at peace with the rugged mountain country which is our home. Together we delight in spring rain, endure summer drought, harvest autumn crops and survive winter winds. It is enough.

But, for one of my sons it is not enough. He is the clever one. Always wanting to know the reason why; forever asking questions which no-one can answer, not even the village elders. Restless and rebellious he argues with his father and is forever at odds with his brothers.

'That boy of yours will come to no good,' my neighbours say.

'They are jealous,' I tell myself, 'he is a fine boy with a good head on his shoulders.' But secretly, I worry that they may be right. My son has a wild streak; the passion of a zealot. He hates the Romans, who govern us.

My son finally finds someone he can respect in Jesus, the teacher. It is wonderful to me. Here, at last, is someone who does not fear his questions: someone who treats him seriously and answers him wisely: someone who gives him a focus for all his energies. I am so happy that the teacher chooses my son to be one of his closest travelling companions.

My, how he travels! Visiting places and seeing sights I can only dream about. For months at a time he is away. When he comes home I see a change. He is calmer, more controlled. A fire still burns in his eye but, like a wild animal, he has been tamed.

'One day,' he tells us, 'when the time is right, my Master will raise up his army and overthrow the Romans.'

My husband grunts, 'Is that what he says?'

'That is what he says.'

'Where is this army?' my husband asks. 'Where does he keep it, so well trained and so well concealed that it can overcome the might of Rome?'

'My Master will call down the hosts of heaven and the people will rise up in rebellion,' my son retorts, 'when the time is right.'

'Oh,' my husband replies, looking keenly at my son. 'And when will that be?'

'When the time is right.' My son is angry.

His father stirs the fire thoughtfully, then quietly comments, 'I thought this teacher of yours was a man of peace.'

'You do not understand,' my son says fiercely, 'you never understand. You know nothing!' And he storms out of the house.

My husband shakes his head. 'I am not sure that boy of ours knows what he has got himself into.'

I feel afraid, refusing to accept the possibility. I want to believe that the improvement in my son is permanent. I have put my hope in the teacher's strange powers. After all, everyone speaks well of him, . . . well, nearly everyone. Some claim he has a demon. I cannot believe that. He heals the sick, gives sight to the blind and hearing to the deaf: he even talks to women and plays with children. I have seen him. Surely such a man will not lead a rebellion? I do hear, but I do not believe it, that he can raise the dead, turn water into wine, subdue storms and even walk on water! Well, you cannot believe everything you hear! . . . What is certain is that he can do many wonderful things; but the miracle, to me, is that he tamed my son.

Now things change. My fears return as my son's mood darkens. He loses what little interest he has in family affairs; spends his time wandering in a distracted state about the village. I hear him muttering to himself, 'How long? How long?' He becomes morose and edgy.

Unable to contain my anxiety any longer I make up my mind to speak to the teacher myself. I search him out when he is alone, sitting on a grassy slope looking out to sea. I say, 'teacher, I am concerned about my son. He causes me much sorrow because he is not like other men. At first, when he followed you, he was transformed. It was wonderful. For the first time in his life he seemed content. I could hardly believe he was the same person. But recently he has changed again; his dark moods have returned, worse than they have ever been. He has grown more restive. More extreme. I am afraid he will do something foolish: something rash; something he will regret. Please, Sir, have a quiet word with him. Will you do that? He listens to you.'

Jesus says nothing but draws pictures in the sand with his finger. His silence troubles me.

'What did I do wrong, Sir? Since he was a small boy I have tried to understand him but an evil demon seems to possess his soul. What have I done that my child was born with this tormented spirit? Have I sinned? Can you help him, Sir, with your secret powers? Can you save him from himself?'

Jesus continues to write in the sand. The silence is unnerving. I begin to wish I had not come. Desperation drives me to say more, 'I hoped, when you chose him to be one of the twelve, that he would change. And he did. For a while. I was so happy. But now I see a frenzy in him, like a fever, devouring him. It frightens me.'

His fingers stop moving, and silently he studies the pictures he has drawn. Then, very carefully, he wipes them away with his hand, smoothing the sand over until there is no trace of the images he made. Now his silence is like a gentle breeze on a summer evening.

Finally Jesus turns to look at me. His eyes meet and hold mine with uncomfortable intensity, yet . . . I no longer feel afraid.

'Neither you nor your husband have sinned,' he says sadly. 'To love is to suffer. Whether as mother, father, child, lover or friend we are most hurt by those we most love. You gave your son life, the most precious gift. Whenever we truly love, we give life. But we cannot control the life we create by our love. Each one of us has a path to tread. Each one of us must choose the way we take for ourselves. We cannot be responsible for the choices our loved ones make.' He sighs. Then, slowly he continues, 'You trust God and you have chosen the right path but your son will choose another way. You are not responsible for that. Mother of Judas, your son will break your heart; and mine, too. We can do nothing about that. We can only love him and pray for him. And we must trust that the loving purposes of God cannot be overcome by evil.'

That is what he says to me. It is as clear to me now as if he is sitting beside me still. But he is not. It is the Sabbath and I am sitting here alone: numb with shock and grief.

Yesterday the Romans came and took Jesus the teacher and crucified him. I saw his tortured body hanging there, on that hideous cross. They tell me it was my son who put him there. Then my son, the child I love, went and hanged himself. I cannot bring myself to mention his name. It is too much to bear. Nothing will ever be the same again.

But it is the Sabbath. Tomorrow, at daylight, I will go with the other women to anoint the body of the teacher. It is the least I can do. Then . . . then . . . I will go to anoint the body of my son, Judas.

### PRAYER

*Almighty God, Heavenly Father, who freely gave your son, teach me that true love does not cling possessively, nor seek to control. Give me grace to hold, as on an open palm, those I love without making any conditions at all. Help me to bear the pain which such love must sometimes suffer. For Jesus' sake. Amen.*

### Suggested reading

Matthew 10.1–25, 34–37; 26.14–16, 47–50; 27.3–5.

The Society for Promoting Christian Knowledge (SPCK) was founded in 1698. It has as its purpose three main tasks:

- **Communicating the Christian faith in its rich diversity**

- **Helping people to understand the Christian faith and to develop their personal faith**

- **Equipping Christians for mission and ministry**

SPCK Worldwide serves the Church through Christian literature and communication projects in over 100 countries. Special schemes also provide books for those training for ministry in many parts of the developing world. SPCK Worldwide's ministry involves Churches of many traditions. This worldwide service depends upon the generosity of others and all gifts are spent wholly on ministry programmes, without deductions.

SPCK Bookshops support the life of the Christian community by making available a full range of Christian literature and other resources, and by providing support to bookstalls and book agents throughout the UK. SPCK Bookshops' mail order department meets the needs of overseas customers and those unable to have access to local bookshops.

SPCK Publishing produces Christian books and resources, covering a wide range of inspirational, pastoral, practical and academic subjects. Authors are drawn from many different Christian traditions, and publications aim to meet the needs of a wide variety of readers in the UK and throughout the world.

The Society does not necessarily endorse the individual views contained in its publications, but hopes they stimulate readers to think about and further develop their Christian faith.

For further information about the Society, please write to:
SPCK, Holy Trinity Church, Marylebone Road,
London NW1 4DU, United Kingdom.
Telephone: 0171 387 5282